The Rightful Place of Science:
Designing Knowledge

The Rightful Place of Science:
Designing Knowledge

Clark A. Miller
Tischa A. Muñoz-Erickson

Consortium for Science, Policy & Outcomes
Tempe, AZ, and Washington, DC

THE RIGHTFUL PLACE OF SCIENCE:
Designing Knowledge

The Rightful Place of Science series explores the complex inter-actions among science, technology, politics, and the human condition.

For information on The Rightful Place of Science series, write to: Consortium for Science, Policy & Outcomes
PO Box 875603, Tempe, AZ 85287-5603
Or visit: http://www.cspo.org

Other volumes in this series:

Halpern, M., Eschrich, J., and Sadowski, J., eds. 2017. *The Rightful Place of Science: Frankenstein*. Tempe, AZ: Consortium for Science, Policy & Outcomes.

Lloyd, J., Nordhaus, T., Sarewitz, D., and Trembath, A., eds. 2017. *The Rightful Place of Science: Climate Pragmatism*. Tempe, AZ: Consortium for Science, Policy & Outcomes.

Model citation for this volume:

Miller, C. A., and Muñoz-Erickson, T. A. 2018. *The Rightful Place of Science: Designing Knowledge*. Tempe, AZ: Consortium for Science, Policy & Outcomes.

ISBN: 0999587730

ISBN-13: 978-0999587737

FIRST EDITION, JUNE 2018

CONTENTS

Preface: Organizations and the Challenge of Knowledge   i

1   The Cost of Knowledge Failures   1

2   How Organizations Make Knowledge   23

3   Designing Knowledge Systems that Work   53

4   When Different Ways of Knowing Conflict   73

5   Creating a Knowledge-Aware Organization   105

Conclusion: Taking Control of Knowledge   141

Acknowledgements   145

Notes   149

About the Authors   163

PREFACE: ORGANIZATIONS AND THE CHALLENGE OF KNOWLEDGE

This is a book about how to improve the design and use of knowledge.

In the 21st century, knowledge is an organization's most important asset. Companies, government agencies, and civic groups spend enormous resources on knowledge to inform and support crucial decisions, to guide strategic planning, and to prepare for the future. High-quality knowledge is even more valuable if organizations want to improve performance, maintain legitimacy, and thrive in an era of constant change and perpetual surprise. How can organizations ensure that they have high-quality knowledge?

We argue in this book that the quality of knowledge is a direct result of how that knowledge gets made. Yet remarkably few organizations have a clear idea of how their knowledge is constructed. Most still believe strongly in a logic of discovery. Knowledge is found, they assume — not conceived and constructed out of the organization's own values, routines, and operating assumptions, both explicit and hidden.

This belief leaves many organizations effectively in the dark, ignorant of unforeseen threats or potential opportunities, and vulnerable to errors, mistakes, misunderstandings, misperceptions, misinterpretations, and other knowledge failures. Ask the banks caught up in the subprime mortgage crisis in 2007. These institutions took for granted the ratings of mortgage debt securities, without fully inquiring into how risk estimates were derived and the conditions under which they might turn out to be incorrect. As a result, they lost hundreds of billions of dollars, and they harmed the world's economy.

Or ask the cities currently confronting increasing risks of infrastructure failure due to floods, heat waves, and other nasty weather events. For the past century, they have embedded historical weather data into their standards for infrastructure design. Unfortunately, as a result of changes in weather and climatic patterns, those data are an increasingly poor predictor of the future conditions those infrastructures will experience. In the words of the National Weather Service, as they watched Hurricane Harvey's rapid intensification and record rainfall in Houston in 2017, future weather events are likely to be "unprecedented." Yet no city in the United States, except perhaps New York, dealing with the aftermath of Superstorm Sandy, has systematically reevaluated its use of weather and climate data for future infrastructure design.

The stakes involved in designing and applying knowledge systems to complex problems and challenges are enormous. We argue that organizations need to pay careful attention to how knowledge is made if they want to avoid serious failures. This means understanding and evaluating knowledge systems: the people who make knowledge and the routines and practices through which they generate, validate, communicate, and apply that knowledge in and outside an organization. The design and function of these systems matter: what assumptions they make, how they treat uncertainty, what analytical processes they use, what evidence they draw on and what standards they use to evaluate it, how much effort they put into verification and what strategies they use, who has access to the resulting knowledge (and who should have it), and many more important questions.

Going further, we argue that knowledge systems should be designed with an eye toward the organization's diverse stakeholders, to serve the needs of all the communities that the organization touches. This is particularly important when the knowledge produced underpins decisions with broad social ramifications. Simply put, the lack of information has become too easy of an excuse for many organizations. In the face of today's complex and often rapidly changing realities, organizations have a responsibility to work with their stakeholders to carefully review and evaluate how they create, collect, analyze, and apply knowledge and, where necessary, to invest in significant upgrades and improved designs. By doing so, they will improve their own performance, avoid costly mistakes, and help their knowledge systems become more valuable, robust, and forward-looking.

The design of knowledge systems must be done carefully, of course. The rise of "big data" has made many knowledge systems vastly larger, more complex—and more difficult to unpack to understand and track where knowledge comes from, how it gets made, what it means for the organization, and how to effectively put it to use. New approaches to knowledge design also have the potential to open up data (e.g., about customers) to inappropriate access to individuals within or outside the organization. Understanding and upgrading knowledge systems can improve privacy protections, increase cybersecurity, and avoid the kinds of problems with knowledge systems hijacking that Facebook and other social media sites increasingly confront. Close attention to the detailed design of knowledge systems is especially important given the rapid growth of data-centric enterprises, the Internet of Things, artificial intelligence, and autonomous vehicles and systems, all of which rely on properly functioning knowledge systems for their effectiveness, the success of their business models, and the safety of their customers.

On the other hand, failing to pay sufficient attention to knowledge systems can instead lead to tunnel-vision. Many organizations have discovered in recent years that they possess overly narrow accounting and finance systems, for example, which neglect a wide variety of alternative, but valuable, indicators of potential organizational performance, such as sustainability and social responsibility. These improved metrics could help social enterprises, government organizations, and profit-making corporations equally well. In short, if organizations design knowledge systems that "count" more relevant things, they will be positioned to make improved decisions about the things that matter most.

This book provides a guide to understanding, analyzing, evaluating, and improving organizational knowledge systems. We provide basic frameworks that explain the structures and elements of knowledge systems, their functions, and the potential complexity of their dynamics. And we offer insights into how organizations can become more aware of — and actively manage and upgrade — their critical knowledge systems.

1

THE COST OF KNOWLEDGE
FAILURES

Alongside people, knowledge is an organization's most important asset. The drive to create new knowledge is essential for all organizations. Investments in new data and information systems are growing rapidly in the public and private sectors, as organizations seek new ways to improve their performance through better knowledge creation, acquisition, and use. The U.S. government spends $130 billion each year to fund research and development. Companies focused on knowledge—Google, Facebook, Apple, Amazon, IBM, Intel—have grown to become the world's largest and most powerful. Control over intellectual property is now a key element of success for many sectors of the economy. Smart devices, smart systems, and big data are transforming consumer technologies and business processes, driven by massive investments in artificial intelligence and information infrastructures. For national security agencies, intelligence and surveillance are crucial tools in the fight against global terrorist networks. We live in a world awash in ideas, information, and data. It is increasingly common to hear people use labels like "knowledge organizations," "knowledge societies," "knowledge economies," and "knowledge warfare" to describe aspects of the world that we inhabit today.[1]

1

Yet given the rapid proliferation of data and information systems, and perhaps to some degree because of it, knowledge failures are surprisingly persistent. In recent decades, knowledge has shown up time and again as a prime culprit in major failures of public policy and business decision making. Numerous high-profile social, economic, and political catastrophes have been caused by failures either to know what was happening or to act properly on knowledge that was available. These failures have occurred despite the growth of highly sophisticated knowledge systems in many kinds of organizations. In the United States alone, even a partial list of major knowledge failures is enough to catch one's attention: Pearl Harbor, Three Mile Island, the Challenger explosion, the misidentification of Iraqi weapons of mass destruction, the fight over ballot counts in the 2000 Presidential election in Florida, the terrorist attacks on September 11, 2001, Hurricanes Katrina and Sandy, the 2008 financial collapse, the Deepwater Horizon oil spill, the ongoing saga of debates about the evidence of climate change, and regular hacking of sensitive digital data.[2] Other countries routinely experience similar problems.

Of course, knowledge failures come in far more mundane varieties, too. As individuals, we miss appointments — often because we forget to look at the calendar or forget to write them down in the first place. Sometimes our investment choices work out; sometimes they do not. Knowledge of what makes for a healthy diet proliferates, with thousands of diet books available for purchase on Amazon. Yet many people still exhibit poor nutritional habits. We routinely buy things only to discover that we could have bought them for less at the store down the street or at a different internet site. We have a global epidemic of knowledge failures, big and small.

The Italian philosopher Niccolò Machiavelli often gets a bad rap as the patron saint of amoral scheming and plotting for power. But his major point was quite simple: making good decisions requires high quality knowledge.[3] To act without good knowledge is to chance being foolish, or worse. Leaders, whether in business or government, make choices every hour using uncertain, incomplete, and incorrect knowledge. Those choices routinely risk serious management and policy failures. In the face of these risks, Machiavelli argued that leaders should focus on collecting and using knowledge wisely to enhance their likelihood of making good decisions. Today's advocates of big data make a similar argument: only organizations that can find new and innovative ways to collect and act on today's vast data streams will set themselves up for success.[4] But the ongoing pervasiveness of knowledge failures suggests that the problem is bigger than just gathering as much data and information as possible. The real problem is to design and act on knowledge effectively, even in the face of the increasing complexity and uncertainty that confront today's organizations.

The idea of designing knowledge may be surprising to some. Engineers design technologies. Architects design buildings. Artists design sculptures. But do scientists or data analysts design knowledge? In a word, yes. This book's primary message is as simple as Machiavelli's: what we know and what we don't know are shaped by the arrangements we put in place — or fail to put in place — to construct and design knowledge. Knowledge doesn't just appear by magic. Rather, knowledge is a product of what we call knowledge systems: the organizational practices and routines that make, validate, communicate, and apply knowledge.[5] In turn, knowledge systems filter, manipulate, and represent the data and information that come out the other end.

In today's world, in which labels such as "post-truth" and "alternative facts" have proliferated, it is crucial that organizations that want to be successful understand how knowledge actually gets made. Knowledge systems frame which questions get asked and which don't. Just as importantly, they frame how questions get asked. They determine the methods used to answer those questions. They define assumptions. They establish burdens of proof. They demarcate strong from weak evidence. They decide whether to review or validate data and, if so, who does the review and how. They lay out how to decide when knowledge is uncertain and what to do if it is. They set limits on the boundaries of relevant expertise. And they set priorities for investments in new knowledge.[6]

Taken altogether, the design and operation of knowledge systems thus has enormous consequences for the knowledge that ultimately emerges and appears in front of people making decisions. Knowledge systems shape what we know and what we don't. This is true for individuals, businesses, and governments. Even when knowledge professionals — people whose positions require them to attend carefully to making and using knowledge — do not make design choices explicitly, they do so tacitly, grounded in cultural, organizational, or disciplinary assumptions about how best to make knowledge. Only by thoroughly understanding the dynamics and organization of knowledge systems can leaders and the knowledge professionals who support them reduce the number and intensity of major knowledge failures. Our goal in this book is to help you learn how to do just that.

Dissecting Recent Knowledge Failures

Our perspective on knowledge systems puts us directly at odds with one of the world's oldest ideas, that true knowledge impartially and objectively reveals underlying facts about the world. If we have the facts, some might say, we know enough. We don't need to know how we got them.[7] But most of the time, people and organizations are

4

not dealing with true knowledge, in the philosophical sense of this phrase. Rather, organizations confront knowledge claims: uncertain propositions whose relationship to truth cannot be easily or directly ascertained. In such circumstances, how knowledge gets made, reviewed, communicated, and used—the social processes of knowledge production—matter enormously. Through a deeper understanding of processes of knowledge production and the knowledge systems they are embedded in, knowledge professionals can get a much better grip on the knowledge their organizations possess, on organizational processes for creating, validating, and using knowledge, and on the strengths and limitations of both.

To be sure, scientists, data analysts, and others who produce knowledge generally have a good sense of process. Often, however, their sense of process stems from intuition rather than careful analysis. Worse, documentation of knowledge-making processes is often poorly communicated alongside data and research findings. Knowledge producers may also sometimes keep exact information on knowledge-making processes to themselves. And, in any case, it is knowledge users—people who are making hard decisions based on uncertain knowledge claims—who ultimately must understand knowledge systems and processes of knowledge production if they are to be fully cognizant of the strengths and weaknesses of the knowledge claims they are applying.[8] We believe it is important, therefore, for those who manage and use knowledge to have a better understanding of the knowledge systems on which they rely.

The dangers of misunderstood or misapplied knowledge have never been starker. In recent years, major knowledge failures have created widespread pain for many people. For example, the people of New Orleans, Louisiana, faced an inundated city for over two years due in significant part to faulty knowledge systems underlying the design and maintenance of their levees. The people of Flint,

Michigan, were poisoned when the knowledge systems meant to protect them allowed them to be exposed to lead, whether through deliberate manipulation or simple neglect of monitoring systems that should have identified and rectified the problem much more quickly. And we now know that millions of U.S. workers lost their jobs in the financial crisis due to failures within the banking sector to properly know and understand the risks of new financial products.

Over time, however, these and other problems have led to an even deeper crisis in knowledge systems as everyday people have become increasingly skeptical of the ability of experts to identify, analyze, and develop proper responses to the problems that confront the world.[9] In the UK Brexit debate over whether to leave the European Union, the rejection of experts and expert knowledge was a significant factor in the final outcome of the vote, as the British people declared that they no longer trusted experts to guide decisions in ways that would improve their lives and livelihoods. Beyond the UK, anti-expert sentiments have helped to fuel growing populist sentiments against the politics of austerity in the European Union and in the backlash against elites in the United States on both the left and the right. In each of these cases, it is increasingly clear that expert knowledge systems are diverging significantly from those of other people who are no longer persuaded that experts understand or account for everyday realities in expert analyses.

It is worth looking in more detail, therefore, at how knowledge failures occur.

Financial Collapse

In 2008, U.S. financial markets collapsed, leading to one of the worst recessions in U.S. history and a decade of global financial repercussions. One key cause of this collapse was a series of knowledge failures by banks and bond rating agencies. Debt markets for mortgages have been around since the 1970s, allowing banks to package mortgages into debt securities that could then be sold to others. According to the research of historian Donald Mackenzie,[10] early in the development of these debt securities, banks developed relatively robust knowledge systems for assessing the risks associated with any given security. Banks reviewed each individual mortgage that comprised a security. This review gave the buyer a great deal of insight into how risky the underlying mortgages were and, in turn, the risks involved in buying and owning those securities.

Over time, however, debt securities evolved into more complex offerings, called collateralized debt obligations. These new securities packed hundreds or even thousands of times as many mortgages together and then broke the resulting packages up into multiple debt securities. Theoretically, these securities were much safer because of the way they distributed risk more broadly, and were even compared by some observers to government debt (which is considered the safest form of debt). As a result, more institutions purchased them in higher quantities, helping to finance the rapidly growing sub-prime mortgage market in the early 2000s.

Subsequently, two problems arose in how banks, ratings agencies, and regulators assessed the risks of this market.

First, the risk models used to evaluate the new debt securities turned out to have a rather severe flaw. These models theorized that the new securities were much less risky in part because they distributed risk across millions of mortgages, not just a few hundred or thousand as had earlier mortgage-backed securities. However, this assumed that risks of default were uncorrelated across individual mortgages. Unfortunately, this turned out to be an incorrect assumption under particular circumstances, such as a nationwide slump in housing markets combined with a nationwide economic recession that undercut the ability of people across the country to pay their mortgages on time (especially those holding sub-prime mortgages). When that happened in 2007, the risk of default on these securities rose rapidly and banks suddenly owned enormous assets whose value began to drop precipitously.

Second, banks were paying less attention to collecting detailed risk knowledge on their assets. Under their original risk knowledge system for mortgage-backed debt securities, banks might still have been aware of the risks if they had tracked the underlying risks in individual mortgages. However, the scale of the new debt securities, with each containing portions of millions of individual mortgages, made that all but impossible. Investors no longer had the organizational capacity to closely assess the risk of the securities they were purchasing. So, in the face of theoretical models that insisted these securities were much more secure, banks essentially quit monitoring the underlying mortgages at all.

What happened next is equally important to understanding why the financial collapse occurred. The security of debt, whether in the form of bonds, mortgage-based securities, or collateralized debt obligations, is assessed by debt ratings agencies like Moody's and Standard & Poor's. These agencies use debt risk ratings systems based on a comparative assessment of how safe a debt investment is compared to other debt investments. The risk rating of a given debt security is not communicated using a quantitative measure. Rather, each debt security is placed into a category alongside other debt instruments judged to have similar risks. In this system, debt taken out by the U.S. government and other sovereign nations that routinely pay their interest is rated as the most secure debt and given the highest ranking, AAA. At the other end of the scale are so-called junk bonds: debt from companies or other organizations that are at high risk of going bankrupt and defaulting on their debt payments.

As a result of the (flawed) theoretical models of risk used to evaluate the new collateralized debt obligations, some of these securities were rated as equivalent in safety and security to U.S. sovereign debt, i.e., AAA. That category is considered ultra-safe and the risk of default is perceived to be extremely low. When these securities began to default, however, and people in the debt industry began to realize that the risk models were in error, the ratings agencies moved quickly to reassign these securities to higher risk categories, properly moving them from AAA to A or even B or C (effectively junk bonds, in some cases).

Here, however, the comparative nature of the bond rating knowledge system backfired. As banks and other big investors began to see debt securities that had been rated AAA shift to much higher risk categories (amidst a wider recession and concerns about risk in many markets), they began to ask whether other AAA-rated bonds might also be less secure than they had originally thought. In short, confidence quickly bled out of the entire bond market as the credibility of the bond rating system collapsed. The result was a huge drop in liquidity in bond markets, as no one would loan money to anyone else. This seizing up of credit markets was the primary cause of the subsequent U.S. and global financial collapse.[11]

Hurricane Katrina

In 2007, a year before the U.S. financial market collapse, a panel appointed by the American Society for Civil Engineering (ASCE) released their report reviewing "one of the nation's worst disasters ever": the destruction of the city of New Orleans by Hurricane Katrina.[12] In the executive summary of that report, the panel highlighted that organizational decisions were central to explaining why the catastrophe occurred:

A storm of Hurricane Katrina's strength and intensity is expected to cause major flooding and damage. A large portion of the destruction from Hurricane Katrina was caused not only by the storm itself, however, but also by the storm's exposure of engineering and engineering-related policy failures. The levees and floodwalls breached because of a combination of unfortunate choices and decisions, made over many years, at almost all levels of responsibility.[13]

Going deeper, a closer look at the report's detailed analyses finds that the reason organizations made poor choices was primarily poor quality knowledge. The report identifies and discusses several significant knowledge failures, including:

- Engineers designed the floodwalls based on flawed models of the variability of soil conditions surrounding the base of the walls. Making matters worse, they also used a safety factor that was too low to account for the uncertainties that this variability introduced into the design.

- The hurricane protection system, which included a diverse array of levees, floodwalls, pumps, waterways, and other water control technologies, was funded and built on a piecemeal basis. Most importantly, it was monitored, maintained, and operated by diverse authorities, exacerbating the problems arising from its patchwork design.

- The design of the hurricane protection system was based on a model of what the U.S. Army Corps of Engineers termed a "Standard Project Hurricane," which characterized the strength and intensity of hurricanes along the Gulf Coast that one might reasonably expect the system to protect against. Unfortunately, the model significantly underestimated the strength of the hurricanes the city could face. Worse, the model was not updated over time, even though hurricanes that hit the city and the Gulf Coast even before the protection system was built were stronger than the model anticipated. Later, the model was still not updated despite growing evidence that hurricane frequency and intensity was shifting in the region, rendering the model obsolete.

- The levees were built too short, based on incorrect data, and grew shorter over time as the city sank relative to sea level.

- The design of the hurricane protection system was not reviewed by an external group of engineers.

- Managers and policy leaders failed to effectively communicate the risks associated with the hurricane protection system to the public, leaving many people with poor knowledge of the real risks they faced living in the city.[14]

Learning from these failures, the ASCE panel argued, requires better knowledge practices and knowledge systems. Among their top recommendations:

- Build system-level assessment of the risks involved.

- Communicate those risks effectively so that the public understands them.

- "Rethink the whole system" by reevaluating how the current hurricane protection system assesses and manages risk and whether that approach is adequate.

- Improve knowledge about the dynamic state of the hurricane protection system and the threats it faces.

- Enhance coordination among the diverse agencies involved in the system to ensure that each knows what the other is doing.

- Put a single individual in charge so that both the involved agencies and the public know who is in authority, while that person can create and act based on system-wide knowledge.

- Ensure that outside experts are involved in reviewing the engineering analyses, designs, monitoring, maintenance, and operation of the system going forward.

Flint's Water Supply

In 2015, lead was discovered in the water supply of Flint, Michigan, after thousands of city residents were exposed to high lead concentrations for over a year.[15] Lead is a dangerous neurotoxin that can create acute problems for adults in high doses and long-term problems for brain development in children, even in relatively low doses. Despite this fact, city water supplies still sometimes rely on lead pipes. Replacing urban water infrastructures is both expensive and disruptive. Instead, pipes are often coated to prevent lead leaching into the water supply. And then, crucially, officials monitor lead levels in water carefully to makes sure people are not exposed. Unfortunately, for a variety of reasons, those measurement systems failed the residents of Flint. Many people ended up with high levels of lead in their water and now confront deep uncertainties about their own and their children's futures.

To understand how the water system failed, we must first begin by understanding how the knowledge system was supposed to work. Water sampling is governed by the Environmental Protection Agency's Lead and Copper Rule, as part of the National Primary Drinking Water Regulations. The Lead and Copper Rule requires that city water utilities collect and test water samples for the presence of lead on a regular basis. The number of samples that must be collected and the frequency of sampling are determined by the size of the community served and whether the city has recently observed higher lead levels. For cities above 100,000 people, for example, 100 samples must be taken and tested every 6 months. The results of those samples are then reported to appropriate state officials who subsequently report them to the Environmental Protection Agency (EPA). These results are then used to determine whether the city's water supply meets or exceeds specified "action levels" that would trigger various required responses. The required limit is 15 parts per billion (ppb) of lead in the 90th percentile sample. In other words, no more than 10% of the city's samples may exceed this 15 ppb amount. Cities that exceed these levels are subsequently required to take a range of actions, including public notification, treatment of source water (if source water is causing the problem), and implementing corrosion control technologies (if corrosion in lead pipes is causing the problem).

This is a classic knowledge system. Specific rules and procedures are laid out for how knowledge is to be acquired (regular sampling), what knowledge matters (how many of the water samples exceed the legal limit), and how that knowledge translates into action (if more than 10% of the samples exceed the legal limit, cities must act). One complicating factor, however, is the organizational complexity of the knowledge system. The Lead and Copper Rule is overseen and enforced by the EPA, but the nation's water quality laws are implemented by state governments, which oversee the activities of local water utilities. In the case of Flint's water supply, the City of Flint operates the water utility and collected the samples for the system. Those samples were then submitted to the Michigan Department of Environmental Quality (MDEQ), which determined whether the city complied with the Lead and Copper Rule and reported the results to the regional office of the EPA.

Also, like in all other knowledge systems, one of the challenges of lead monitoring is that the methods for sampling lead allow for a degree of uncertainty and variability in the sampling. Once the water has been sampled, the methods for testing its lead concentration are relatively standardized. However, the method used to collect water from the tap is known to potentially significantly affect the lead levels in the water sample. For example, using heated water often contributes to higher lead levels. Likewise, running water at higher volumes can flush greater amounts of lead into the sample than if samples are taken at low volumes. Flushing the water before the sample is taken can reduce lead levels. Lead levels are also likely to vary from house to house and neighborhood to neighborhood, based on where lead pipes are located in the city and how much corrosion is occurring within any given pipe. To account for this, cities are required to collect samples from houses that are particularly high risk. Getting good results thus requires getting good samples—and that's not necessarily easy.

Interestingly, in Flint, it appears that water samples were collected by sending sampling kits to residents and asking them to collect samples from their houses. Thus exactly how samples were collected is unknown, although city residents who received the samples have reported the instructions they were given. According to critics of Flint and of the MDEQ, those instructions use methods that are known to underestimate lead levels. At the same time, Flint officials seem to have had difficulty collecting their target number of samples. In response, the MDEQ lowered the number of required samples from 100 to 60, after 71 samples were collected. The MDEQ justified this change as a response to Flint's shrinking population. While in the 2010 census, Flint had 102,000 inhabitants, by 2014 that number had shrunk to just under 100,000, which put it in a different EPA category. Cities over 100,000 are required to collect 100 samples. Cities from 50,000-100,000 can collect only 60.

More troubling is evidence revealed in response to a Freedom of Information Act request. Two of the samples were excluded, bringing the total number of samples to 69. The two samples excluded both showed lead levels that exceeded the legal threshold for action. The reason for excluding those samples is unknown, but the consequence was significant. With those samples, the lead level at the 90th percentile (the legal standard, as described above) would have measured 17 ppb of lead, requiring intervention. Without the two samples, MDEQ determined that the city water had 11 ppb of lead. Eliminating the two samples meant that city residents did not need to be notified of high lead levels, nor did action to reduce lead levels, including anti-corrosion treatments, need to be taken. This decision occurred just as residents were complaining to local public officials in Flint that they were experiencing strange symptoms that they feared came from contamination in the water supply.

These complexities mean that, even in the case of a relatively simple knowledge system such as this, designed to measure a single parameter via a standardized test, there are lots of ways that the system can go wrong. From the perspective of this book, government officials in all three relevant organizations failed in several key ways:

- They failed to exercise proper scrutiny of the knowledge claims emerging from their own knowledge systems, asking whether what they were observing could be mistaken.

- They failed to exercise heightened scrutiny of their knowledge system during a time of significant change (in the case of Flint, a significantly shrinking population and the switch to a new water supply). In all too many cases, we see that knowledge system failures occur when major changes happen in the phenomena being described. Knowledge systems are generally designed to work well under specific circumstances: when those circumstances change, assumptions built into the knowledge systems may change. Thus, changing circumstances represent a time when knowledge professionals need to be most careful.

- They failed to respond to emerging evidence that their knowledge system might not be telling them everything they needed to know, e.g., when residents began to complain about a variety of problems with their water and when some water samples began to show high lead levels. Instead, they either ignored or willfully denied that evidence.

Putting Knowledge Systems Analysis to Work

Reflecting on these three knowledge failures offers a quick introduction to some of the key lessons of this book. The first is that the knowledge available for making decisions is a direct product of knowledge systems design and operation (or their neglect). Because the Army Corps of Engineers relied heavily on the Standard Project Hurricane model, their designs could not be better than the quality of the model. As hurricane patterns in the Gulf changed, the model failed to keep up. Because water managers working for the city of Flint and the state of Michigan failed to properly implement lead monitoring systems and refused to accept other evidence, their residents were exposed to significant lead poisoning.

Thinking that "truth is truth" is a poor approach for knowledge managers who inevitably operate in a realm of uncertainty and change. Far more helpful is to view knowledge as a set of claims about the world and how it works (or people and how they work). These claims are the output of social and institutional routines and practices. Whether they are correct or not is always uncertain, at least to some degree. Knowledge managers cannot ever fully trust their data, although they may feel confident at times that they have the best basis for a decision that they can at the time.

The second lesson, therefore, is: the quality of knowledge is also a product of the design of the knowledge system that produced it. Bad knowledge system design will result, more times than not, in lousy knowledge claims. Bad knowledge system design is thus potentially very expensive for organizations that will inevitably be forced to make decisions based on poor quality information. Of course, good knowledge system design can also be expensive, especially because it involves, as we will discuss more deeply later, routines designed to regularly or even continuously evaluate the quality of the knowledge being produced and to update the knowledge system where required. Many of the strategies recommended by the ASCE after Hurricane Katrina, for example, would have been expensive. And the resulting insights won't ever eliminate uncertainty. But if decisions put people's lives, property, or money at risk in a significant fashion, the extra cost of a high-quality knowledge system can reap enormous rewards.

A third important lesson is that the quality of a knowledge system is a result of both knowledge practices and social and institutional practices. Selecting the best methods in the world doesn't help if they're applied sloppily, if a knowledge enterprise has the wrong skills, or if the external reviewers brought in don't have the necessary expertise to make sure methods get used properly. Conversely, hiring top-notch knowledge systems practitioners is likely to create a much better sense of the circumstances under which organizations can and cannot rely on knowledge systems, regardless of the underlying quality of the work itself, since they will be able to give a good read on what the quality level is. Put differently, the real bite of this lesson is that the social and institutional practices of knowledge systems—the people parts—are every bit as essential to good knowledge systems as the methodologies and the data systems. As we will see, this is partly about people's skills as scientists or data experts, but only partly. It is also about:

- Their savvy as knowledge systems designers and operators.

- Their ability to effectively communicate to and work with others in the organization to assess the nature of the problems they face and the knowledge they must generate.

- Their ability to help others understand the meaning and significance of knowledge with respect to the decisions others need to make.

- And, finally, the routines and practices the organization puts in to place to identify, review, monitor, stress-test, upgrade, and innovate its knowledge systems.

A fourth lesson is that many knowledge systems matter, not just an organization's own knowledge systems. Whether as individuals or organizations, we inhabit a world of diverse knowledge systems. Sometimes those knowledge systems leave gaps, where no one has created knowledge that could be highly useful. In other cases—as with diet advice—everyone seems to have very different ideas about how to be successful. Sometimes, some people believe the science is compelling—e.g., on climate change—while others believe it's nonsense. This is, unfortunately, the reality of the world we currently inhabit. One of the key lessons about knowledge systems is that how knowledge systems get organized—in terms of both the knowledge content and the social and institutional practices—shapes the results. In rare cases, multiple knowledge systems may create overlapping agreement. In most cases, however, they create diverging interpretations of what might seem like the same facts.

This diversity in knowledge systems can be valuable. By mixing different ways of looking at problems, different ways of gathering evidence, and different methods for reviewing data and conclusions, we can often get a richer picture of what is occurring. But this diversity can also exacerbate underlying conflict, mask that conflict behind apparent scientific uncertainty, or even create the appearance of uncertainty where none exists. We can also get situations like the hurricane protection system, where different parts of the system fail to coordinate their knowledge and actions. Managing the complexities of multiple, interacting knowledge systems is one of the central challenges of the 21st century and another test of high quality knowledge systems practices and professionals.

Given the multiplicity of contemporary knowledge systems, it seems fair to conclude, fifth, that one of the biggest dangers is getting trapped in a single paradigm or culture of knowledge system design and operation. This was the central problem in Flint, Michigan. And, although it isn't necessarily called out in the ASCE report, another knowledge failure that created major problems in the case of Hurricane Katrina was the fact that engineers allowed themselves and others to believe that the problem of risk was one solely of engineering analysis and design. Two other fields of knowledge could have provided vitally important insights. Climate modelers have speculated for some time that hurricane strength and intensity in the Gulf of Mexico may change over time as the sea surface temperature in the region warms. And, ecologists knew key ecosystems that provided natural protections against storms had eroded over time in the Mississippi River delta. The failure to incorporate these elements into models of the hurricane protection system reflected an epistemic culture that proved unfortunately narrow.

The final lesson of the book, therefore, is that knowledge system managers and practitioners need to practice reflexivity and adaptability in the design and operation of their knowledge systems. Reflexivity is the ability to critically investigate the shortcomings of knowledge systems, including when those shortcomings will and will not matter. Adaptability is the ability to modify and innovate those knowledge systems over time to adjust to changes in the phenomena about which one is producing knowledge or the questions to which the knowledge is meant to provide an answer. Perhaps the most egregious knowledge failure associated with the destruction of New Orleans was simply that most of the underlying elements of the knowledge system had received relatively little attention or updating for a very long time. Seriously reviewing and updating the knowledge system might have revealed that the hurricane protection system had glaring weaknesses, which would have caused significant political problems. And, it might not have done any good, given the long lead-time for new infrastructure investments. Nonetheless, if we're in it for the long haul, careful, ongoing, systematic attention to the adequacy of knowledge systems is highly significant.

The Outline of the Book

These six lessons orient the rest of the book. Acquiring knowledge about knowledge systems is not always straightforward. The practices that we use to make knowledge are often hidden from plain view, even to those who are producing or using this knowledge. Less obvious are the cognitive and cultural dispositions that shape how groups and institutions think. Often, we take for granted how we know what we know. We need guides and tools to help us uncover how knowledge systems work. Much like journalists use a variety of sources to put together a story, or an archeologist uses material and textual tools to dig up evidence from the past, knowledge systems analysis uses different conceptual lenses and approaches to map, measure, and critically evaluate knowledge systems. In the rest of the book, we provide a set of pragmatic tools for analyzing knowledge systems.

Chapter 2, "How Organizations Make Knowledge," defines knowledge and knowledge systems and maps the key components or elements that make up the design of organizational knowledge systems: knowledge, values, epistemologies, and structures.

Chapter 3, "Designing Knowledge Systems that Work," describes the key functions that knowledge systems carry out: knowledge generation, knowledge validation, knowledge communication, and knowledge application.

Chapter 4, "When Different Ways of Knowing Conflict," provides a picture of the complexities that arise in the work of knowledge systems because they are dynamic, not static, and plural, not singular. Knowledge systems are functioning, operating enterprises, with all of the internal complexities that entails. They evolve and change over time, in relation to internal and external stimuli, producing new kinds of knowledge (and even, sometimes, forgetting old ones). And they interact with one another in dynamic encounters, contests, and collaborations.

Finally, in Chapter 5, "Creating a Knowledge-Aware Organization," we look at some of the broader contexts and implications of knowledge systems analysis, with an emphasis on how individuals, knowledge professionals, and organizations can build a strong capacity for reflexivity in their design and use of knowledge systems.

Chapter 1 Takeaways

- Knowledge systems are the organizational practices and routines that make, validate, communicate, and apply knowledge.

- Knowledge failures have been responsible for major breakdowns in public policy and business decision making, including the 2008 financial collapse, the destruction of New Orleans by Hurricane Katrina, and lead poisoning in the water supply of Flint, Michigan.

- The knowledge available to any organization or institution for making decisions is a direct product of knowledge-systems design and operation.

- The quality of knowledge is a product of the design of the knowledge system that produced it; bad design will produce poor-quality knowledge claims, and vice versa.

- The quality of a knowledge system is a result of both knowledge practices and social and institutional practices.

- Multiple knowledge systems can interact, overlap, and create competing interpretations.

- One of the biggest dangers for an organization is getting trapped in a single paradigm or culture of knowledge system design and operation.

- Knowledge system managers and practitioners need to practice reflexivity and adaptability in the design and operation of their knowledge systems.

2

HOW ORGANIZATIONS MAKE KNOWLEDGE

How do organizations design and make knowledge? The purpose of designing knowledge is not, of course, to cherry-pick facts or to generate fake news. Rather, it is to know what we know, how and why we know it, and what we don't know—and to make choices about these things deliberately. In its simplest terms, therefore, designing knowledge entails designing a knowledge system that we know and understand.

A knowledge system is a set of organizational routines and practices for creating and using knowledge. More specifically, we define a knowledge system as a set of routines and practices through which an organization or a network makes knowledge, reviews and validates it, communicates it, and applies it in making decisions. In each of the next three chapters, we describe a different aspect of knowledge systems and knowledge systems analysis. In this chapter, we describe the key components of an organizational knowledge system, the things out of which it is made and the elements that help define the ways it makes knowledge and the kinds of knowledge it makes. In our model, there are four such components: knowledge (its content and its associated uncertainties), values, epistemologies, and structures. A first step in knowledge systems analysis, design, and redesign is to map these components.

In his book *The Knowing Organization: How Organizations Use Information to Construct Meaning, Create Knowledge, and Make Decisions,* Chun Wei Choo[1] makes the argument that all organizations—political, civic, or economic—are "knowing" organizations. In other words, organizations are fundamentally made up out of a variety of different kinds of knowledge and ways of knowing. How an organization uses information to construct meaning, create knowledge, and make decisions is all part of the way that the organization creates an identity, establishes a shared (internal and external) context for action, makes sense of its environment, and anticipates and adapts to changing conditions.

Choo's framework is powerful because it identifies the crucial importance of knowledge and ways of knowing for all organizations. But it's not sufficient. We need to take this idea one step further to avoid knowledge failures. We must also know what kinds of knowledge are important and how well the routines and practices of an organization's knowledge systems are doing at producing, validating, communicating, and applying that knowledge. That requires the ability to identify and map the organization's knowledge systems.

Mapping Knowledge Systems: An Overview of Key Concepts

Knowledge system mapping begins with defining the boundaries of the relevant knowledge system. This is never a simple task, as we will discuss in more detail. As with many systems, knowledge systems are often open systems, meaning their boundaries with their environment are porous and elements internal to the system are closely coupled with those external to it.[2] For knowledge systems analysis, bounding the system typically means drawing somewhat arbitrary boundaries and then paying attention during the analysis both to what is crossing those boundaries and to whether key features of the system are getting neglected because of the way the boundaries were chosen.[3] For the purposes of this book, we tend to draw boundaries around knowledge systems either in relation to a specific form of knowledge or practice of knowledge making (e.g., packaged food retailers are required to include nutritional knowledge on packages) or a particular organization that produces knowledge (e.g., the U.S. Census Bureau). This tends to reduce the analytic complexity, which has benefits but also comes with costs, as we will explore further in Chapter 4.

The next step is mapping the knowledge produced by the knowledge system. Knowledge mapping is a commonly used framework in the field of organizational management as a tool that reveals the strengths and weaknesses associated with knowledge management and sharing in an organization.[4] For knowledge systems analysis, however, knowledge mapping must go beyond this idea to examine the content and types of knowledge being produced and to describe what the knowledge system knows as well as what it doesn't know (e.g., the tacit and explicit uncertainties that surround knowledge claims, as well as the kinds and varieties of knowledge claims that the knowledge system might produce, but doesn't for one reason or another).

In this book, when we use the word knowledge, we mean knowledge claims: statements that purport to offer insights into or facts about the world that we live in, whether natural or social.[5] Most decision-makers, most of the time, aren't dealing with knowledge that they know without a doubt to be unequivocally true. Rather, like detectives, they're dealing with evidence that seems to point in one direction or another. Such evidence might come in the form of estimates, models, analyses, observations, or data. And, like evidence of a crime, these knowledge claims need to be evaluated and interpreted to be understood and used appropriately. Our contention in this book is that understanding where knowledge claims come from and how they were developed and shaped by knowledge systems will improve the ability of decision-makers to make sense of and use those claims effectively.

A couple of examples may be helpful. A knowledge claim that can be found on the side of a popular box of breakfast cereal, for instance, might be that "one serving contains 9 grams of sugars and 0 grams of saturated fat."[6] Specifically, this purported fact about the world is found in the product's nutritional label and asserts that someone who eats the cereal for breakfast will consume 9 grams of sugar and 0 grams of saturated fat. This knowledge claim has two purposes. It complies with U.S. law, which requires nutritional information to be published on every food product sold in the country's grocery stores. It also helps consumers make good nutritional choices by selecting healthy food, which is why the government requires its publication.

There are important uncertainties[7] associated with this claim, however. One is the relative size of a serving in the nutritional calculation compared to how much of the cereal an individual consumes. A bowlful is never exactly the same amount of cereal. Most people don't measure carefully how much cereal goes into the bowl. And there's no guarantee that any given bowl's contents match exactly the sugar content of the sample used to generate the box information. Another uncertainty involves the nutritional impact of consuming 9 grams of sugar at breakfast. Nutritional needs vary a great deal depending on the individual's gender, body size, health, and activity level. The sugar in one cup of cereal will mean different things to an active athlete and someone with diabetes. Still another uncertainty surrounds the feature of this knowledge system that fat levels less than 0.5 grams are rounded down to 0 grams. So, in fact, we don't know that the product contains no saturated fat. We only know that it contains between 0 and 0.5 grams — which becomes a very notable source of error if someone consumes multiple servings daily. Only by understanding the full range of uncertainties associated with the knowledge system that produced the claim, as well as the larger context of decision making, can an individual deciding whether to buy this cereal get a good sense of what this knowledge claim really means and how to apply it to improving his or her personal nutrition and health.

Here's another knowledge claim: "the 2010 Census enumerated 308,745,538 people in the United States."[8] The U.S. Census Bureau presents this number to this degree of precision because the U.S. Constitution requires it to generate an exact count. If you read the fine print, however, the Census Bureau acknowledges a wide variety of small errors that creep into its counts, and the Bureau routinely publishes updates. Those errors are the inevitable results of the methods used to sample populations; the rate at which they can get people to complete their surveys; uncertainties people have about how to answer questions; mistakes or deliberate falsehoods people make in answering questions; births and deaths that occur during the counting process; and numerous other design choices. For many applications, these errors will be too small to matter. But for other applications, these errors may turn out to be significant.

It's also important to recognize that knowledge claims are not simply facts or factual claims, the way we usually think about facts. Instead, they are hybrids that blend facts and values.[9] This may seem absurd. Isn't the number of people who live in the United States an objectively true statement about the world? If, hypothetically, we could stamp out all sources of error and uncertainty, it might be possible to generate an entirely accurate measure at a given instant. But it's also a particular fact: namely, it's the number of people who inhabit the United States. The question of who falls into this categorization is very value laden. Put differently, the Census reflects a value choice about which population to count. This value choice, as well as the choice of how to subdivide the United States into its constituent geographic parts for counting, too, is so important that the Census Bureau devotes an entire report to it, the *Geographic Areas Reference Manual*.

One example of this choice is that, until 1900, Native American tribal areas and communities within the United States were not counted in the Census. Today, they are, even though many reservations now exercise important aspects of sovereignty. The Census knowledge system also must decide whether to count citizens, permanent legal residents, temporary residents, undocumented residents, or Americans living abroad temporarily but planning to return. These are all categories of people who could potentially be counted. The Census Bureau makes these choices, sometimes guided by Congress, sometimes by the courts, and sometimes on their own. The Census makes other value choices, too, like which races and ethnicities to break out for special sub-counting.

Returning to our previous example of nutritional information, requiring food retailers to measure and report on packages the amount of sugar and fat in cereals is also a value-laden choice about what information consumers should have access to regarding the foods they buy.

Knowledge claims are also products of epistemologies, or ways of knowing and reasoning about the world.[10] For example, if someone wanted to determine the population of a city, he or she could attempt to count the city's inhabitants or build a model that would estimate the population based on certain input parameters. Modeling (or simulation) and observation are very different ways of knowing, or epistemologies. The resulting knowledge would be quite different, as would its potential sources of error and misinterpretation.

Similarly, Brian Wynne, who studied the relationships between different types of knowledge, has documented a case of conflict between two knowledge systems seeking to assess a problem confronting a community of sheep farmers.[11] One knowledge system sought to develop a computational model of the problem and collect quantitative data that could be used to validate the model. Another knowledge system, by contrast, aimed to prioritize the voice of community members in documenting their stories about what the problem was about, why it was happening, and what could be done about it. Each thus relied on very different epistemological foundations. Each made knowledge in different ways. Not surprisingly, the two knowledge systems generated very different insights into the problem, while also making very different kinds of mistakes.

Finally, knowledge systems are also composed of people who do things—what we call the structures or, more broadly, the social and organizational arrangements, networks, and institutions that comprise a knowledge system.[12] It is crucial to identify where within a knowledge system particular knowledge is located: who knows what; where data is generated and stored; and how, where, and to whom it flows as it is processed, handled, shared, and used.[13] At the same time, knowledge system mapping requires understanding how the people involved in knowledge systems are organized, trained, evaluated, and rewarded for their work. As we will discuss in significantly more detail in Chapter 3, for example, the U.S. Census knowledge systems comprises a huge suite of social and institutional arrangements that include a federal agency—the U.S. Census Bureau—and all of its employees, including tens of thousands of temporary workers that the Census hires on a short-term basis to go out once every ten years to knock on doors and get as many people as possible to fill out the Census survey. The process these individuals use must be meticulously designed and validated by statisticians, and then the individuals must be carefully trained in its use. Methodologically, bringing on that many people all at once and ensuring they all collect data using the same practices and assumptions is a critical challenge that can systematically impact data quality. In turn, the resulting data must be carefully analyzed, synthesized, and disseminated to the many researchers and organizations that use it for a variety of purposes. All of this requires people with different kinds of education, training, knowledge, and skills to perform both individual and collaborative functions well. And that, in turn, requires meticulous attention to social organization.

An Example of Knowledge Systems Mapping

In the rest of this chapter, we want to take the process for mapping knowledge systems laid out above and work it out in greater detail for a specific example. We will focus on the knowledge system developed to support the 1992 United Nations Framework Convention on Climate Change (UNFCCC). Signatories to the convention pledged to begin developing strategies to reduce their contributions to global warming. To do that, countries needed to be able to measure those contributions to provide a basis for holding each other accountable for their agreed reductions. Thus they needed a new knowledge system. This knowledge system was designed to measure the respective contributions of each country to global warming by compiling an inventory of each country's emissions of greenhouse gases, such as carbon dioxide and methane. Greenhouse gases are defined as those pollutants which, when released or emitted into the atmosphere, trap solar radiation and so heat the atmosphere and contribute to global warming.

In the language of the UNFCCC, the countries put in place the broad outlines of such a knowledge system:

> *All Parties, taking into account their common but differentiated responsibilities and their specific national and regional development priorities, objectives and circumstances, shall: (a) Develop, periodically update, publish and make available to the Conference of the Parties, in accordance with Article 12, national inventories of anthropogenic emissions by sources and removals by sinks of all greenhouse gases not controlled by the Montreal Protocol, using comparable methodologies to be agreed upon by the Conference of the Parties.[14]*

Each country that is a signatory to the treaty (known as a Party) is responsible for creating a specific knowledge product: a national inventory. This product should contain certain kinds of knowledge describing "anthropogenic emissions by sources and removals by sinks of all greenhouse gases not controlled by the Montreal Protocol." Anthropogenic means, in this case, human activities that generate emissions of greenhouse gases into the atmosphere (sources) or that remove greenhouse gases from the atmosphere (sinks).

In other words, each inventory will count the emissions by a country that come from human activities, subtract out the emissions by that country that come from anthropogenic sinks, and then report the total. These knowledge claims are to be generated using specific epistemologies, namely "comparable methodologies." These methods are not specified in the treaty. Rather, they are to be agreed upon by the signatories to the treaty at some future point, presumably before the inventories are created. Structurally, the treaty calls for each signatory to produce knowledge (meaning there will be groups in each country, probably within its government, responsible for producing such an inventory), to periodically update it, and to make it available to other countries. The system also puts responsibility on a new organization, the Conference of Parties, to set the rules for how the system works. Elsewhere, the treaty defines the Conference of Parties as an annual assembly of representatives from the countries that have signed the treaty.

Mapping the Boundaries

With this outline in place, we can begin to sketch a knowledge systems map. Just like mapping a city begins with drawing the city limits, mapping a knowledge system begins with delineating a boundary around the object we are trying to describe and analyze. This is not always straightforward. In this case, we might begin to bound the system by saying that we want to include all activities involved in the creation and sharing of national greenhouse gas emissions inventories among countries, including setting the rules for creating these inventories. This would involve the work of the units assigned by countries to produce their national inventories and the work of the Conference of Parties to set the rules. Looking deeper, however, the boundaries become a bit fuzzier. Even before the treaty was signed, another organization, the Organization for Economic Cooperation and Development (OECD) in Paris, had begun working to put together a plan for countries to develop and test national greenhouse gas emissions inventories. Based on their initial work, which involved several countries developing inventories using quite different methodologies, the OECD determined that establishing a standard set of methods would be essential to an effective knowledge system. The OECD then began to establish and convene scientific working groups to determine the best methods to use for each part of an inventory. Later, the Conference of the Parties asked a different group to take over this task. They determined that, since the OECD membership does not include many countries that signed the treaty, the OECD was an inappropriate organization to coordinate the development of standard methods for all countries. Instead, the task was assigned to the Intergovernmental Panel on Climate Change (IPCC).

Should the work of the OECD and IPCC be included inside the boundary for the purposes of creating our knowledge systems map? What we see here is some of the complexity that can arise in knowledge systems, especially in trying to figure out where system edges lie. Because of this complexity (which we will discuss further in Chapter 4), the deeper one goes into knowledge systems analysis, the more frequently one finds a complicated web of connections, which makes drawing appropriate boundaries a difficult and nuanced task. In this case, the answer depends pragmatically on what one is trying to determine with the system analysis. If the analyst is merely trying to judge the knowledge system as it works today, then the work of the OECD and IPCC can probably be considered external. For the most part, their work was done in the past, and the methodologies they established are now accepted as the default practice. If, however, the analyst is interested in examining the strengths and limitations of the standard methodologies, the alternatives that might once have existed but no longer do, or is interested in why this system takes the shape and form that it does, then the work of the OECD and IPCC would more likely need to be incorporated into the knowledge system mapping.

Another question of boundary drawing arises in the work of producing the national inventories. Officially, a government ministry typically carries this work out. In some countries, however, including the United States, much of the actual work is contracted out to other organizations. Should these other organizations be included in the knowledge system? Similarly, the inventory development team generally does not produce most of the knowledge incorporated into the inventories. Instead, most of the knowledge is taken, adapted, and synthesized from published scientific research. Do the scientists who conducted and published the original research need to be incorporated into the map and the analysis? Do the organizations that funded that research need to be included, as their priorities may have influenced, for instance, what knowledge is available to draw on in inventory development? Again, the answer is going to depend a lot on why a knowledge system map is being generated. In some cases, it will be important to draw the system boundaries very widely. In other cases, a narrower boundary may facilitate a more effective analysis.

Many of the boundary questions that arise will be social or organizational in character, meaning that the question will be whether to include the work of additional organizations, groups within organizations, or parts of networks within the system, or to treat them as external to the analysis. Other boundaries may be also significant, however, including conceptual boundaries or separating knowledge into discrete compartments of an organization. As an illustration, there might be reasons to be interested in isolating one aspect of a knowledge system for close attention. In the case of national inventories of greenhouse gases, for example, it might be possible to examine the knowledge system for measuring carbon dioxide emissions separately from its equivalent for emissions of methane or other greenhouse gases (perhaps because the sources of the different gases are often very different kinds of processes and are measured using very different approaches).

Mapping the Contents and Uncertainties

Once we delineate the boundaries of the system for the purposes of a given analysis, the next step is to map the contents of the knowledge within the knowledge system. What is known? What is not known? Or, more specifically, what kinds of knowledge claims does a given knowledge system generate, what are the uncertainties associated with those knowledge claims, and what are the gaps in the knowledge produced?

The task of mapping knowledge is generally relatively straightforward, although it can be a large task if the system is producing a variety of different kinds of knowledge. This is due to the need to understand the character of knowledge being produced in each case. What precisely is known? In the case of the UNFCCC, the produced knowledge consists of greenhouse gas emissions inventories: systematic documentation of the emissions of greenhouse gases into the atmosphere by each country.[15] No country, however, has technology capable of measuring these emissions directly for the whole country. Instead, these inventories are compiled from estimates of the emissions of each gas from a large variety of different types of sources (and, if appropriate, also any sinks that remove that gas from the atmosphere). So, for example, an inventory will typically include estimates of emissions of carbon dioxide from the burning of different kinds of carbon-based fuels (such as gasoline, diesel, jet fuel, etc.) as well as from the burning or cutting down of forests (which releases carbon from the trees). An inventory will typically include estimates of emissions of methane from sources like cattle agriculture (cows burp methane), rice agriculture (bacteria in the wet soils of rice paddies are a vibrant producer of methane-rich "swamp gas," which can escape via hollow rice stalks and other pathways), natural gas pipelines and drilling operations (which often leak), and landfills (which are another good breeding ground of methane-producing bacteria).

Generally, none of these quantities are measured directly, either. Each is produced via various models and formulas that first estimate a typical emission rate for the activity in question and then multiply that rate by an estimate of the total activity within a country. For example, methane released by rice agriculture is calculated by first computing the rate at which methane is estimated to escape from paddy soils (e.g., per square meter of paddy). This value is generated through a synthesis of various scientific studies that have measured this quantity using diverse methods. Second, the emissions rate (often called an emissions factor) is multiplied by the total area of agricultural land planted in rice in the country. So, what the inventory produces is not an actual measurement of national emissions (as, for example, one might if one was using a device installed on a smokestack to measure the emissions from a power plant or factory) but rather a synthesis of best guesses of what emissions might be that are then tallied up to generate a national total.

These estimates have highly variable uncertainties associated with them. Assessing various forms of uncertainty within a knowledge system is also an important part of conducting a mapping exercise. Uncertainty comes in a variety of different forms in knowledge systems. One form of uncertainty arises from the random behavior of the subject the knowledge system seeks to know. Weather predictions, for example, are partly uncertain because the weather is random at some level, i.e., deterministic predictions literally cannot be made.

Much more commonly, however, uncertainty arises from limitations in the tools used within the knowledge system.[16] In the case of the knowledge systems developed by countries to inventory greenhouse gas emissions, most of the uncertainties derive from limitations in the tools. To directly measure greenhouse gas emissions is prohibitively hard, expensive, and time consuming. Uncertainties in these systems depend largely on the quality of government, scientific, and other statistics. In the United States, for example, estimates of fuel burning are generally derived from surveys of companies that sell those fuels, and those estimates are considered fairly accurate: they generally have around 10% error rates for the most commonly and widely used fuels. This accuracy comes from both the careful work of the Energy Information Administration, which conducts the surveys and has an extensive budget and expert statisticians to do so, as well as from the relatively well-known and standardized combustion processes involved in the fuel use. Burning the same amount of fuel in the same engine generally produces pretty close to the same amount of carbon dioxide, allowing for relatively accurate estimations. By contrast, methane emissions from rice agriculture are extremely uncertain (perhaps incorrect in the United States by a factor of 2 or more) due to the relative paucity of scientific data and, more importantly, data on the distribution of agricultural practices that can significantly impact the rate of methane emission from the fields. Studies have shown that different management techniques, for example, can affect emissions rates by a factor of 100 for a given field. While the Department of Agriculture collects reasonably accurate information about total acreage of rice cultivation in the United States, it knows relatively little about the specific management practices used in those fields from year to year. In other countries, uncertainties may be higher, due to less available funding for data collection (the United States is particularly lavish in its funding on government statistics).

Explicit and tacit assumptions that are built into knowledge systems are another source of uncertainty.[17] Most of these assumptions are related to value choices involved in either simplification or specification of the knowledge system, which will be discussed in the next section. Other assumptions may relate to measurement protocols. Early on, for example, in scientific research to study methane emissions from rice agriculture, it was assumed that measurements could be made during short periods and then extrapolated for the entire time the paddy was wet. Scientists assumed that the methane was being released directly from the soil into the water and then into the air, as for example happens when you walk in a swamp and bubbles of methane gas come up around your feet. It was later discovered, however, that rates vary dramatically at different times of the growing season because a large portion of the gas escapes through hollow rice stalks.

There are also broad unknowns in the inventories.[18] Unknowns are simply things that the system does not measure. Some countries literally have no data to include on emissions of some gases from some sources. Estimates of sinks also often have unknown elements. The most important activity that takes carbon dioxide out of the atmosphere is the growing of forests, yet the growth of such forests is notoriously hard to measure, as is the amount of carbon taken up into the forest. If the forest is very well defined, such as a specific plot of land, it can be relatively easy to measure the size of the trees and estimate the carbon content. However, a lot of the carbon is taken up into the roots and the soil, which is much harder to estimate accurately. And what if the tree growth stems from hundreds of thousands of individual households planting (or cutting down) trees? How can that be estimated? More unknowns can be found in the non-emissions impacts on climate of cutting or planting forests, such as the role of forests on the Earth's albedo (how much sunlight the Earth reflects back into space) and weather circulation (due to changes in regional humidity and rainfall patterns). These are entirely ignored by the current treaty knowledge system.

Mapping Knowledge System Values and Standards

All knowledge systems are constructed around key values or standards that help define the foundations of knowledge production in the system.[19] As we noted above, knowledge claims are always hybrids of facts and values.

In the process of creating knowledge, value choices are put together with factual claims to create hybrids through integrated processes of simplification and specification. Simplification refers to the process of creating simplified representations of complex social and/or natural processes. All knowledge systems offer representations that inevitably are less complex than the underlying reality that they represent. Moreover, the values embedded in the knowledge system play an important role in determining which aspects of reality to simplify and to what extent. How much simplification is acceptable? Which aspects of a problem can be simplified and which not? What norms or values should guide the simplifications taken in arriving at knowledge claims? Specification, on the other hand, refers to the need to make broad normative principles more specific in order to fit the particular case(s) with which a knowledge system is grappling.

In the case of the knowledge system of the UNFCCC, we have already seen simplification at work. Instead of trying to measure methane emissions from every rice paddy, countries estimate what is happening to an average paddy and then multiple by the acreage of paddies. This simplification rests on at least two sets of values, one about what kinds of scientific simplifications are acceptable and a second about how much effort is required of countries in compiling their inventories. Both decisions have been ratified by a declaration of the Conference of Parties that this method is acceptable for use in national inventories produced for the treaty.

Specification, by contrast, involves a two-level exercise: first, to specify the broad normative principles that will guide inventory construction and, second, to specify further these broad normative principles regarding the specific cases encountered in the development of inventories. With respect to the broad normative principles, the treaty language quoted above identifies at least nine major values declared as the core principles for the knowledge system:

1. It is Parties to the Convention, and not some other entity, who will create a national inventory report, and they will send the report to the Conference of Parties.

2. Each Party will develop and publish its own report.

3. Parties will periodically update their reports; how often is unspecified.

4. These reports will detail national inventories, rather than sectoral, regional, or provincial inventories.

5. Reports will include only a country's anthropogenic contributions to climate change, not its natural ones. (The biggest implication of this is that only some aspects of forests are considered anthropogenic; other aspects of forests are not. Several disagreements have occurred between countries over definitions of what is and is not considered anthropogenic.)

6. Reports will inventory greenhouse gases, but not other causes of climate change (such as large-scale land use change that impact the Earth's albedo), and only those greenhouse gases not controlled by the Montreal Protocol (precisely which gases this entails is left unspecified in the treaty).

7. Reports will include both emissions and sinks of greenhouse gases, as opposed to just emissions, allowing countries to offset emissions with sinks.

8. Reports must be produced using methodologies that are comparable, which is also to say that they need not be identical.

9. The Conference of the Parties must agree upon what is to count as comparable methodologies.

During the subsequent development of standard methodologies by the OECD and IPCC, these values had to be further specified or defined to determine their precise meaning for controversial cases. For example, rule 5 specifies that only anthropogenic and not natural sources would count. An interesting dispute arose, however, over whether deer should count as anthropogenic sources. Deer burp methane, just as cows do. In the United States and Europe, deer are considered wild animals and thus part of nature (hence, not anthropogenic). In many parts of Africa, however, deer are farmed (as they also are in small numbers in the United States). More importantly, deer populations in the United States are highly controlled through the allocation of hunting permits by state regulatory agencies. Thus one might argue—and several African countries did—that deer should count as anthropogenic as well. The process of defining the knowledge system had to specify whether deer counted as anthropogenic or natural. Similar questions had to be sorted out for forests. What aspects of forest growth and decline count as natural and which as human-caused?

In another case, which involves the role of values in both simplification and specification, a dispute arose between scientists from two countries in the context of making estimates of carbon emissions from the cutting down of forests. The commonly adopted model assigned responsibility for carbon emissions to any country within whose boundaries a forest was cut down. This is a gross simplification, however, because unless the forest is burned, the carbon dioxide is not immediately released into the atmosphere. Instead, most of it stays bound up in the wood from the trees or in the roots in the soil. Eventually, if these are let to stay around to rot, much of the carbon will be released into the atmosphere, but this could take decades. On the other hand, if the wood is built into, say, a house, the carbon could stay bound up in the house for a century. The scientists working on the problem argued with each other over a series of meetings about how accurate the system needed to be to properly assign responsibility for the timing of emissions. Some wanted to prevent deforestation and so to hold countries accountable for all forests cut, regardless of what happened to the wood. Others argued that simply measuring forest cutting would generate misleading information about actual emissions and would distort markets for wood products, like houses, that could bind carbon into fixed forms for decades or even centuries.

The values challenge posed by specification became significant in this case for a second reason. Because carbon could remain bound up in wood for some time after the forest was cut down, large amounts of carbon could be shipped from one country to another before the wood was burned or allowed to decay. In that case, whose inventory would have to take responsibility for counting the emissions: the country that cut down the forest or the country that imported and ultimately burned the wood? This question was highly salient, and the answer depended on the policy goals to which the knowledge system was being applied. Slowing deforestation by deterring countries from cutting down their forests could only be done by allocating responsibility for emissions to the country within which the deforestation occurred. For another group of scientists, however, the goal was to achieve carbon neutrality. For that purpose, replacing fossil fuels with biofuels could be a beneficial strategy. Under this latter set of values, you wouldn't want to discourage countries with forests from cutting them down and exporting them to other countries that could then burn the biomass in power plants instead of coal.

Mapping the Epistemologies

The next element in a knowledge systems map, epistemologies, emphasizes the ways of knowing that shape the content of knowledge.[20] The epistemologies of knowledge systems include a diversity of elements, such as how systems frame problems; the styles of reasoning, forms of evidence, and argumentation they prefer; their ontological classifications; the deeper imaginaries that inform them; and the information technologies they use to collect, analyze, synthesize, and validate knowledge claims. At base, the key question is: "How do we know?" The focus on epistemologies also includes a significant emphasis, however, on "What kinds of things do we know about?" Both are important for knowledge systems analysis. Recent scholarship has also emphasized the significance of attending to deeper cultural structures of thinking that shape knowledge making and decision making. Science and technology scholars Sheila Jasanoff and Sang-Hyun Kim refer to these as socio-technical imaginaries: the forms of social and cultural imagination that shape how people envision the kinds of knowledge they need, how to acquire that knowledge, and how to connect that knowledge to solutions to societal problems.[21]

We define framing as the set of perceptual lenses or worldviews that guide the interpretation and definition of problems, which in turn give shape to the knowledge used to analyze and attempt to find solutions to those problems.[22] As the final example in the previous section suggested, the policy objective of assigning responsibility for greenhouse gas emissions can be framed in terms of deterring actions that contribute to warming or in terms of promoting and incentivizing the adoption of technological solutions that are carbon neutral. Under many circumstances these two framings come out the same, but in others, they do not. More broadly, climate change may be framed as a problem of global pollution, requiring knowledge of the global total of pollutants being dumped into the atmosphere, those responsible for pollutant emissions, and potential technologies to be used to control them. Under that framing, the kinds of emissions inventories developed by the knowledge system we've been describing are essential for holding countries responsible for their emissions. By contrast, climate change may also be framed as a problem of long-term changes in the weather, requiring knowledge of how weather patterns are changing, the impacts of those changes on the economy or society, and strategies for adapting to those changes to minimize the resulting harm. Framed that way, we'd need a radically different set of knowledge systems.

Styles of reasoning refer to how knowledge systems contemplate, analyze, and reason about what they know.[23] In simple terms, this can be thought of in terms of the preferred methodologies used by a knowledge system for generating knowledge and arguments. It connects very closely to the forms of evidence the system collects and uses, as well as the forms of argumentation used within it. Differences in styles of reasoning often reflect differences among the kinds of experts or forms of expertise present in a knowledge system. For example, scientific knowledge systems often rely extensively and exclusively on quantitative and statistical information, while indigenous knowledge systems draw more extensively on oral histories and personal observations and experience. Variations in reasoning styles have been observed in both scientific and political cultures,[24] and even within science, scholars have documented quite distinct styles of reasoning.[25]

Analysis of the epistemology of a knowledge system should also include consideration of the ontology of the system and its information technologies. By ontology, philosophers refer to the kinds of objects about which a knowledge system generates knowledge. That architecture is often embedded in the methods or tools used to analyze, communicate, and represent data and information. As Geoffrey Bowker and Susan Leigh Star have demonstrated, the specific design of information architectures reflects and embeds extensive social values that significantly shape the kinds and especially categories of knowledge ultimately generated by knowledge systems.[26]

For example, under the UNFCCC, greenhouse gas emissions inventories categorize the world in terms of certain kinds of objects:

- Countries (not businesses or individuals): United States, France, India, China, etc.

- Greenhouse gases (but not other kinds of human activities that impact the climate): carbon dioxide, methane, nitrous oxide, etc.

- Sources and sinks of emissions (defined as the proximate human activities that release chemical gases into the atmosphere or take them out; not, for example, their underlying causal drivers, such as population growth), e.g., for methane: leaks from pipelines and gas wells, cattle agriculture, rice agriculture, etc.

In any knowledge system based on counting, as the emissions inventories are, ontology is centrally the things being counted and the categories into which those counts are broken up.

Finally, it may be important to understand the deeper forms of imagination that shape the operation of knowledge systems.[27] The examples given above of the methodological developments within the knowledge system of the UNFCCC reveal not only its epistemology, ontology, and information infrastructure but also aspects of its deeper imaginative foundations. As a physical phenomenon, for example, emissions of greenhouse gases into the atmosphere occur distributed across the face of the planet. Since it would be impossible to capture and count each and every emission at each and every point on the Earth's surface, inventories must simplify this complex reality. One aspect of this simplification is to aggregate emissions on a nation-by-nation basis. Not surprisingly, given its origins in international diplomacy, the imagination of this knowledge system ultimately privileges nations as the primary actors — even as cities, states, and other forms of social organization have become more ambitious agents in pursuing greenhouse gas emissions policies. As we observed above, nations are a primary element in its ontology.

Yet how does the knowledge system imagine the nation? Numerous strategies could be used for determining which emissions should be counted by which country. The one chosen is primarily geographic. With few exceptions, nations count emissions that fall within their boundaries. But this rule is not stated anywhere, and there are alternatives. For example, inventories could document how many emissions result from supply chains that provide a nation with the goods and services that its citizens consume. By this method, many of the emissions that physically occur in China would be counted in the U.S. inventory, since many of the products made by Chinese factories are ultimately bought by U.S. citizens. Another approach would assign responsibility for emissions to the country whose people or institutions were responsible for them. U.S. tourists and U.S. army deployments around the world both are responsible for many greenhouse gas emissions, but these are not accounted for in the U.S. emissions inventory. Neither of these options was taken, in favor of counting based on the physical location of the emissions within the sovereign territory of a nation. The imagination of the nation as a geographic entity was so deeply rooted in the ways that scientists and diplomats thought about the world that alternatives were never seriously considered. It only arose when it became clear that certain emissions, especially from fossil fuels burned by ships and airplanes, occurred in international waters and thus couldn't be easily counted as belonging to a particular country.

Mapping the Structures and Flows of Knowledge

The final element is to map the structure and flows of knowledge within the knowledge system. By structure, we refer to the social, organizational, institutional, or network arrangements of the knowledge system. How are the people who do the work of the knowledge system organized? In the case of the knowledge system for national inventories of greenhouse gas emissions, the treaty requires that each country produce and publish its own inventory. This task is generally carried out by one or more government agencies, either in-house or contracted out to a third party. Individuals within these agencies generally collect and collate a range of different kinds of data to produce a synthetic overview of the total number of emissions of different greenhouse gases that occur within a country in a given year. In wealthy countries, such as the United States, much of this data is already published by government agencies, and so the task is merely to assemble it. In poorer countries, with less extensive government data infrastructures, pulling together the relevant information may be a much harder task.

When finalized, the inventory takes the form of a written document that contains the appropriate knowledge as required by the agreed-upon methods. This document is submitted to the Conference of Parties. Once submitted, the Secretariat of the Conference of Parties establishes a review committee comprising individuals from other countries who review the document and then enter a series of consultations with the original submitting country. The treaty does not formally mandate a review process to verify the accuracy of the knowledge claims made in a national inventory (although the country may, of course, conduct an internal review of the inventory before it is published, and some do). These reviews are instead part of a capacity-building exercise designed to help facilitate improvements in the inventory generation process through friendly evaluations, knowledge and information exchange, and the creation over time of robust, cross-national networks of knowledge system workers who can draw on one another's expertise and professional contacts to improve inventory quality.

In analyzing the social organization or structure of knowledge systems, it can be useful to keep in mind a few key points.

First, the relationship between knowledge and social organization is generally reciprocal. The structure of social arrangements and knowledge flows within an organization often has a significant impact on the kinds of knowledge that knowledge systems choose to produce (and the kinds they choose not to produce). In turn, the knowledge produced by an organization shapes a range of phenomena, including the kinds and distributions of outcomes that result from social and policy decisions. In other words, the ways that we make knowledge and the ways that we make decisions or take actions are generally not independent of one another but rather tightly coupled. In addition, how knowledge flows through and among organizations impacts who can access and make use of it[28] and thus power asymmetries within or between organizations.[29] Researchers use the word co-production to describe this mutual, bidirectional relationship between knowledge and social organization (we will discuss co-production in more detail in Chapter 5).[30]

Knowledge professionals can use a variety of techniques, such as social network analyses, to map and visually portray how their knowledge systems are structured and what kinds of linkages (e.g., information and resource flows) influence the knowledge produced and used in their organization. Key questions to ask in such analyses include:

- Who knows what within the knowledge system (i.e., who is involved in the generating, reviewing, circulating, and applying of knowledge in the knowledge systems)?

- At what stages are different people involved in the process?

- How are the system's social and institutional arrangements organized?

- How do these arrangements distribute power and authority?

- What consequences flow from these arrangements for the production of knowledge?

Second, one of the striking features demonstrated by recent research is just how varied the social and institutional arrangements can be across different knowledge systems.[31] At one end of the spectrum, highly formal processes such as government scientific and expert committees provide advice on a wide range of policy issues, often under very specific rules and procedures and with tightly constrained organizational processes.[32] The national greenhouse gas emissions inventory system described here is a very formal knowledge system. At the other end of the spectrum, informal knowledge systems may take very different social and institutional forms.[33]

Finally, we would be remiss if we failed to highlight the value of mapping the structure and flow of knowledge systems by tracing the people, places, and processes involved in carrying out the key functions of knowledge systems. These functions — knowledge generation, validation, circulation, and application — are the subject of Chapter 3. This is roughly the approach we took in the first two paragraphs of this section as we described the structure and flows of the national emissions inventory system.

By mapping the work that an organization does that contributes to these functions, analysts can help to locate the social and institutional activities of knowledge systems. Yet as the emissions inventory process shows, tracking how knowledge flows *across* organizations is also important. As we will discuss further in the next chapter, such models are rarely as simple as a one-way transfer between those who produce the knowledge and those who make decisions.[34] Instead, knowledge making and decision making are often distributed across multiple organizations and networks. Understanding how knowledge flows through multiple social actors, and how these distributed structures may be facilitating or inhibiting knowledge flow, can be critical for organizations, especially those with multiple and diverse audiences. Here, social network analysis may usefully supplement organizational knowledge mapping to understand knowledge flows in an inter-organizational landscape and reveal overall systems structure. We will discuss this further in Chapter 4 as an illustration of the complexities that can arise in the dynamic behavior of knowledge systems.

Chapter 2 Takeaways

- A knowledge system is a set of organizational routines and practices for creating and using knowledge. It has four components: knowledge, values, epistemologies, and structures.

- Knowledge claims are not simply facts, but hybrids that blend facts and values. They also include uncertainties, assumptions, and unknowns.

- Knowledge claims are products of epistemologies, or ways of knowing and reasoning about the world.

- Knowledge structures are the social and organizational arrangements, networks, and institutions that comprise a knowledge system.

3

DESIGNING KNOWLEDGE SYSTEMS
THAT WORK

In Chapter 2, we defined knowledge systems in terms of their component parts. Knowledge systems are made up of knowledge (or knowledge claims), values, epistemologies (or ways of knowing), and structures. But what do these knowledge systems do—and how do we make them work properly? All knowledge systems share certain general functions. In this chapter, we divide these functions into four areas of work: knowledge generation, knowledge validation, knowledge communication, and knowledge application. We first offer a brief definition of each function, and then turn to a more extensive elaboration of examples of each through the rest of the chapter, discussing in each case strategies that organizations can use to understand and adjust how knowledge systems are functioning.

The first function of a knowledge system is knowledge generation. Knowledge generation is the act of creating a knowledge claim.[1] What does this mean? In practice, knowledge generation is an exercise in figuring out what is going on or how things work. It is often an act of detective work: collecting data but also making sense of what those data mean. It can be the work of an individual, a team, or a vast enterprise. Its ultimate goal is to be able to say: "This is what is happening." A good example is research, whether that takes the form of scientific research or market research. The purpose is to answer a question.

In general, knowledge generation includes processes of problem formulation, data collection, and data analysis, as well as the reporting of information. Depending on the question at hand, it can also include modeling, simulation, forecasting, or theory development. As a consequence, the ways that these activities are carried out, who carries them out, with what attention to detail, with access to what resources, and using what methodologies varies a great deal across knowledge systems. In the end, however, all of them come together to produce a claim about some piece of knowledge. Mapping and designing systems for knowledge generation, therefore, means figuring out what institutional arrangements and practices create new or updated ideas, and where these systems are located within the organization as a whole.

The second function of knowledge systems is knowledge validation. Knowledge validation consists of the practices, processes, and routines by which knowledge claims are subject to review, critique, assessment, check, and so forth. The goal of knowledge validation is to go from having a knowledge claim to having a knowledge claim that one has some degree of confidence in. Mapping knowledge validation means figuring out who within a given knowledge system is assessing, reviewing, testing, or otherwise cross-checking knowledge that is being generated, circulated, and applied, using what methods and criteria, and whether those current practices are sufficient for the needs of the organization.

Just as knowledge generation practices vary dramatically from system to system, so do knowledge validation practices. In science, for example, labs will often repeat their own work to ensure they get similar results. Most scientific journals require peer reviews of manuscripts by other experts in the field. In journalism, editors typically fact-check stories before publishing them. In the U.S. government, administrative agencies may hold hearings at which stakeholders present competing evidence and interpretations regarding a particular area of knowledge or action. Scientific assessments are formal processes through which a group of scientists will systematically scour the scientific literature on a subject, evaluate the range of claims made, and produce a report synthesizing what they believe to be legitimate knowledge on the subject of the assessment.

The third major function of knowledge systems is knowledge circulation. Circulation refers to the routines, practices, and processes by which knowledge claims are exchanged, transmitted, or translated from one location or group to another. Another word for circulation is communication. We have chosen circulation to emphasize the multi-dimensional character of this activity, and not simply a flow of knowledge from one group or location to another. Knowledge circulation exists within organizations in the form of knowledge flows among those who generate knowledge and those who use it. Knowledge also circulates between an organization and its many stakeholders, including the users and consumers of its products, as well as shareholders, regulators, and others. Mapping and designing systems of knowledge circulation means sorting out who has access to new knowledge claims, through what channels, whether those are the right people, whether the forms of communication that are occurring are properly communicating both appropriate knowledge claims and enough additional information to judge that knowledge and its value, and how to fix problems. Knowledge circulation can also include communications about knowledge claims or knowledge generation and validation processes that happen within or among organizations.

The final function of knowledge systems is knowledge application: the social and institutional practices by which knowledge is factored into decisions. This phase is often also referred to as the use, uptake, or consumption of knowledge. Like the three previous functions, application of knowledge is a complex undertaking that varies considerably across knowledge systems. One facet of application is how knowledge is acted upon (and whether the generation, validation, and circulation functions are being carried out in a way that enables knowledge to be acted upon). Who acts on knowledge? What expectations do they have about the knowledge system? How credible are knowledge claims to users — and to others who care about the decisions and actions being taken? Another facet of application is how uncertainty is expressed (in the context of application), processed, and applied to decisions involving knowledge. What do users know about how knowledge is generated, validated, and circulated and what that means for their decisions? Still another facet of application is how acting upon knowledge reflects back on the organization and on its processes of decision making. How does an organization change as it learns new things?

Of course, these four functions are not independent of one another. Expectations about the use of knowledge inevitably feed back into how knowledge gets generated, validated, and circulated, just as generation, validation, and circulation invariably shape use. Thus, the four functions of knowledge systems are often tightly coupled and intertwined, with each facet of the system reinforcing the others.[2] This can dramatically enhance system efficiency, but it can also constrain the ability of the knowledge system to see outside its own blinders. Mapping out how these interrelated functions work together can thus be an important tool for analyzing the adequacy of existing knowledge systems and designing new ones.

Now that we've defined the four key knowledge functions, let's look at some examples of how each of these four functions works across diverse kinds of knowledge claims and knowledge systems.

Knowledge Generation

Creating a knowledge claim can range from simple to complex. If someone asks where I am going, I can create a knowledge claim on the spot: "I am going to the store." On the other hand, if someone wants to know how sea ice is changing as a result of climate change, the generation of knowledge may be much more complex and time intensive. Based on data collected by satellites and ice cores and analyzed over a 30 year period, for example, the Intergovernmental Panel on Climate Change recently observed that "annual average Arctic sea ice extent has shrunk by 2.7 [2.1 to 3.3]% per decade."[3] In each case, the routines and practices involved in knowledge generation vary dramatically, responding to the very different kinds of knowledge claims being made.

Let's return to the examples introduced in the previous chapter. For both the publishing of nutritional information on food packages and the collection of Census data, knowledge generation begins in U.S. law. Today's nutritional labels are a product of the 1990 Nutrition Labeling and Education Act. This law requires that the U.S. Food and Drug Administration develop and enforce standards for nutritional labeling and that companies properly label the food products that they sell. Similarly, the Census is required by the U.S. Constitution and, in much greater detail, Title 13 of the United States Code (the Code is the compiled law of the United States). These laws require various entities to generate various kinds of knowledge, and they set many of the rules for how knowledge generation must take place (or they determine who gets to set the rules).

All of this highlights a crucial point: knowledge generation often begins long before people collect and analyze data, when decisions are made about how to collect and analyze data, as well as who is in charge of doing so. It also highlights a second important point. Many of today's large and influential knowledge systems have their origins in law or in government policy. This is certainly true in the United States, but it is equally true in most of the world's countries. Information is a necessity for the bureaucracy and administration that currently dominates most forms of government. Even where they do not use the knowledge themselves, many governments have also identified the availability of information for citizen use as important. Thus, for example, the U.S. Securities and Exchange Commission requires that all publicly traded companies publish accurate financial and other information on a routine basis, so that markets are as transparent as possible to investors. The U.S. Food and Drug Administration also requires that any company that desires to market a drug in the United States collect, analyze, and make available to the Food and Drug Administration research on the safety and efficacy of that drug.

Following the passage of the 1990 nutritional labeling law, the Food and Drug Administration developed guidelines for companies to use in generating nutritional knowledge claims. That information is contained in the 1998 FDA publication: *Nutrition Labeling Manual - A Guide for Developing and Using Data Bases.*[4] This guide specifies how to design a sampling plan and collect samples of a food product, how to chemically analyze each sample to determine nutritional content, and how to statistically analyze the resulting data to generate the final figures to be used on the labels. The guide, in turn, requires manufacturers to actually carry out (and pay for) the work to generate nutritional data using the documented methods about several different aspects of their nutritional content. This includes the fat, carbohydrate, and protein composition, the breakdown of fats and carbohydrates, sodium and potassium contents, and various vitamins.

In the case of the U.S. Census, knowledge generation consists of counting and categorizing the country's over 300 million inhabitants and making sure that this number is as accurate as possible. Knowledge generation by the U.S. Census is one of the largest knowledge systems in the United States. The core element of knowledge generation is a survey of all U.S. households that asks people to identify who lives at each address, in every community, across the country. This is necessary because the U.S. Constitution requires that the Census count each person in the United States once and only once. The survey involves hiring hundreds of thousands of employees of the Census Bureau across all fifty states to ensure that all households (or as many as is humanly possible) fill out the survey and do so correctly. This is not an easy task, even for people who've lived in the same house for decades. Someone must maintain a record of addresses and who lives at that address, over decades. Someone else must check to see that the same people are still living in that house, find a time when they are home and can answer the survey questions, and get them to do so. This even carries risks. Representatives of the federal government are not always welcome as visitors by everyone, even when their job is simply counting noses.

As we discussed in Chapter 2, extensive rules govern who is to be counted and where they are to be located for the purposes of the Census. What if someone is staying with a friend because they've just been divorced? What about prisoners, who might be incarcerated far from where they live? Or what about a college student living in a dorm room? Or what about someone who lives on the streets? How do we make sure that each of these people is counted — and only once? And how do we make sure that we count each person in the right place, since the Census also must properly allocate each person to where they live? The routines and practices of Census knowledge generation must have answers to each of these questions.

Each employee who knocks on doors to get people to fill out this survey must thus receive substantial training to ensure that they understand how the survey is to be properly administered and how to find the people they're supposed to count. The resulting surveys must be tabulated to achieve appropriately enumerated counts for every location in the country. The resulting data must be checked and rechecked, through a broad range of procedures of review and evaluation. The total cost to generate the 2010 Census: more than $13 billion.

Not all knowledge systems are this large, of course. Some are small and very simple. As parents, basic knowledge generation about our children's learning is relatively simple. We observe what they do and say. We ask them questions and test their knowledge. And we check in periodically with their teachers. Yet even the simplest knowledge systems are becoming increasingly complex. When we were growing up, knowing which movie to go to on a Saturday afternoon meant looking at the movie page in the newspaper, which showed which movies were showing, at what times, and ads gave a hint of what they were about. One might also occasionally see movie ads or movie review shows on television or talk about movies with friends who'd already seen them. Today, we can go to the web and get a wide range of expert and consumer reviews of any given movie, Wikipedia descriptions of their plot, other parents' reviews, trailers and clips from the movie, etc. The amount and diversity of knowledge generated about films is much more extensive.

Institutions, whether they are families, businesses, communities, or governments, create knowledge because they need or want it as a basis for making decisions. As these examples suggest, especially with regard to the cost of knowledge generation, knowledge does not simply magically appear. Knowledge generation entails work and organization. Knowledge generation involves all of the processes through which data is collected, aggregated, analyzed, and synthesized. These may be developed in-house. In their laboratories, for example, scientific teams are always developing new methods and new tools for observing, measuring, or modeling the phenomena they are studying. By contrast, knowledge generation may be highly standardized, as in the case of nutritional labels regulated by the FDA.

The process of knowledge generation is not simply the work of technical experts in scientific laboratories. Laboratory research and analysis is often a significant part of the process, but only part. As we observed above for the Census, data collection can also involve significant fieldwork, as surveyors travel around communities knocking on doors and encouraging people to fill out their forms. Just as importantly, legal and political work is an essential part of knowledge generation. Congress must write laws governing knowledge production, as they have for the Census and nutritional labeling. And government agencies must, in turn, develop regulatory rule-making processes that determine exactly which data to collect and which methods to use. This activity—involving a wide array of social and organizational practices and routines—comprises the processes through which knowledge gets made. This is why knowledge making can be so expensive—and why big data is now big business.

Knowledge Validation and Review

The second major function of knowledge systems is to review and validate knowledge claims. The validation and review of knowledge claims is often viewed solely in terms of veracity (are the knowledge claims true?) or credibility (how much confidence can we have in them?). However, this perspective is too narrow. Validation and review processes may also focus, for example, on the salience or relevance of knowledge generated by the system to particular audiences. Or review processes may seek to enhance the political legitimacy of the system by drawing in stakeholders to participate in reviews. The choice of which values or criteria are to be served by review and validation processes (veracity, credibility, salience, legitimacy, etc.) is a key design question for every knowledge system.

Review and validation processes can be integrated tightly into knowledge generation or can be separate and independent. Processes of knowledge generation generally contain within them, for example, various routines for assessing the validity of data and insights, ranging from the spot-checking of individual data points to the use of control populations and statistical tests. Going beyond these routine practices, many knowledge systems also have more and less extensive means of independently or externally reviewing and validating knowledge claims. Probably the most widely adopted form of external form of validation is the use of peer review. Both facets of knowledge systems (integrated and independent) can be considered as part of knowledge validation.

Knowledge validation is an essential element in determining the credibility of knowledge claims. This is true in terms of quality assessment (internally to a knowledge system, how good is our knowledge?) and in terms of the perceptions of outsiders of the rigor of the knowledge system (have they taken the time to check their results properly?). While validation practices are no guarantee of accuracy or truth, decision-makers often rely on knowledge validation to give them a greater sense of confidence about the data on which they rely most heavily. The U.S. government, for example, has adopted widespread peer review requirements for government data and information. The caliber of knowledge validation can vary dramatically, however.

Some institutions have highly regarded validation practices, while others are less trusted.

Knowledge validation need not occur solely after the fact, either. In the U.S. government, for example, many organizations fund scientific research, and nearly all use some form of peer review to assess, ahead of time, the quality of the research that scientists propose to conduct. Of all agencies, the National Science Foundation (NSF) is regarded as having the best overall peer review process—a result in part of the rigorousness of its procedures and in part of the caliber of its networks across the U.S. scientific community.

In judging knowledge claims, the rigor of review processes obviously matters, but so do the criteria these processes are designed to evaluate and assess and the capacity of reviewers to evaluate knowledge against those criteria. In the case of the NSF, review processes include both the scientific quality of the proposed research (what the agency calls "intellectual merit") and the potential societal value or impact of the work (what the agency calls "broader impact"). The NSF's goal is to increase the likelihood of generating high quality science that also has high social value. The review process at the agency only includes scientists, however, who tend not to have a great deal of training or experience in evaluating the social value or impact of the science. As a result, review panels run by the agency can fail to give the issue sufficient weight. By contrast, some review panels at the National Institutes of Health include representatives of patient groups, ensuring that the experience and expertise of patients is incorporated into determining which research proposals are likely to have the most impact on improving health outcomes.

In another example, the review processes set up by the Intergovernmental Panel on Climate Change (IPCC) have been designed to ensure that the organization's knowledge claims are widely accepted within the scientific community and of the highest scientific credibility. Thus, the IPCC only allows its authors to use peer-reviewed scientific literature as the basis of its written reports on what is known about the Earth's climate. While this offers an important foundation of quality for IPCC reports, it also means that the IPCC must exclude insights that might be gleaned from information that has not appeared in peer-reviewed scientific journal articles. This may include material published in government reports, by environmental organizations, or that is simply too new to have been peer reviewed.

In both the NSF and IPCC cases, knowledge validation routines and practices involve trade-offs. These trade-offs come in at least two forms. Design choices for knowledge validation processes may select for certain measures of quality while neglecting others (e.g., ensuring research will add valuable new scientific knowledge versus ensuring that it will have important value for society). At the same time, design choices may trade-off one kind of error in knowledge validation for another. High barriers may ensure that only the most reliable knowledge claims pass muster. As a result, however, high barriers may exclude data that turns out to be important but comes from a less credible source. By contrast, low barriers will ensure that a wide range of knowledge claims are included, some of which may turn out to be of lower validity.

So, what about knowledge validation in the cases of Census data and nutritional labels? Let's start with the Census. Census data is critical to U.S. policymaking. Both the U.S. Constitution and U.S. law allocate resources, from seats in Congress to federal grants for alleviating poverty, based on U.S. Census population data. The accuracy of Census data is thus both of paramount importance to many stakeholders and potentially politically controversial. At the same time, as we've already observed, the Census is all but guaranteed to miss some people, or to locate some people at the wrong address, especially in dense urban areas with lots of people. How can the Census use knowledge validation practices to help address these challenges?

One answer that has been suggested is to use statistical methods to correct the Census count. For the past several decades, a debate has swirled over whether the Census should use statistical sampling techniques that would allow them to correct their enumerated counts. If one merely needed an agreed upon, relatively accurate estimate of the U.S. population, such estimates wouldn't matter very much. But since the Census is being used to allocate political and financial resources, many people support the idea of generating as accurate a count as possible and correcting for known deficiencies in survey methodologies that tend to result in greater errors in urban population counts. So far, however, the Census has not used such methods in determining how many people live in the United States. The reason is that the U.S. Constitution requires an "enumeration" of the U.S. population, which the courts have interpreted as meaning that each person must actually be counted. No estimates or corrections allowed, even if it can be demonstrated that their use would improve the accuracy of the count.

Because of the political significance of its counts, the U.S. Census Bureau has established a procedure that allows other organizations to raise questions about its work and have those concerns reviewed. The 2010 Census Count Question Resolution Program specifically allows government leaders to challenge the population counts generated by the 2010 census. This review mechanism may be used to correct a range of errors in the collection, counting, and processing of census data, although the Census Bureau will not collect additional data. As of March 26, 2015, two hundred thirty-nine communities across the country had issued challenges, with the bulk being resolved through a modest change to the Census count.[5]

The U.S. Food and Drug Administration has also created a procedure for reviewing company data as part of its nutritional labeling program. Companies submit the proposed labeling information, the raw data underlying that information, and information on the methodologies used to formulate the information to the FDA. The FDA will then use the information submitted to essentially check the math of the companies, verifying that their own recalculations match the labeling information submitted by the company. The FDA will also review any further studies that the company plans to pursue to analyze the nutritional value of foods. Finally, the FDA will provide a written response to the company documenting the outcomes of its review. The FDA does not, however, directly review the accuracy of the company's measurement systems, e.g., via inspections or conducting their own experiments on food content.

In both the Census and nutritional labeling programs, we see an important aspect of knowledge validation, namely the question of who carries out the reviews. In both cases, the primary knowledge generation organization conducts significant knowledge validation activity to ensure the accuracy of the resulting information. In both cases, however, additional parties are also authorized to pursue reviews of the resulting data and to formally challenge the results and ask for additional review. This is a common feature of knowledge systems. The National Science Foundation asks independent scientists who work for universities, companies, and national laboratories to review proposals that it receives for funding. Likewise, the IPCC asks the world's governments to review its climate change assessment reports; it requires report authors to document their responses to each review item; and it then hires independent editors to review author decisions. Most importantly, the IPCC insists that governments review and agree collectively on the precise wording of its "Summary for Policymakers" documents for each report—although the reports themselves are not so treated. Knowledge validation can be very complex.

Knowledge Circulation and Communication

Knowledge that has been generated and validated does little good if it is not circulated and communicated. This was one of the earliest insights of the scientific revolution in the 17th century, where scientists took advantage of the newly invented printing press to create journals that circulated new scientific findings much more widely and quickly than ever before. Within science, knowledge circulation or communication is primarily carried out through informal and formal mechanisms for knowledge sharing within the scientific community, such as conferences and meetings, pre-publication archives, and scientific journals. Also crucial is how science is communicated more broadly, including popular science publications, science museums, K-12 classrooms, magazines published by industry or activist organizations (e.g., for policy-relevant environmental knowledge), science news stories in the mainstream media, books about science, and increasingly blogs and other web-related content. Even within a single organization, it is crucial to understand the circulatory systems that convey knowledge from place to place. Finally, knowledge circulation must include the contexts in which knowledge is shared and debated among citizens and publics, from dinner tables to coffee house conversations.

We might also want to look at the circulatory system for knowledge in and around the policy process. Modern governments have established extensive formal and informal mechanisms for collecting, aggregating, synthesizing, and reviewing knowledge claims of all sorts, circulating those claims, and bringing them into the policy process. Congressional hearings offer one example. Congressional committees organize formal events, which may run from a day to many months, at which invited speakers present formal testimony to Senators and/or Representatives and their staff. These events are televised and available to the U.S. public. Also, at the formal end of the spectrum, U.S. law makes provision for a range of scientific advisory committees to assist in the work of U.S. government agencies. For example, the Science Advisory Board of the U.S. Environmental Protection Agency has a variety of duties, including reviewing the scientific work of the agency and providing advice to the Administrator. The U.S. Administrative Procedures Act also requires that government agencies host administrative hearings associated with agency rule-making exercises at which a variety of stakeholders may present their understanding and interpretation of scientific evidence bearing on agency decisions. The United States has also organized the National Academies with an eye to soliciting, reviewing, and circulating knowledge claims on high profile, policy-relevant issues. The emphasis of U.S. policymaking on knowledge has also created a vibrant culture of knowledge generation and circulation among think tanks, academic research centers, and industry organizations that surrounds these more formal enterprises.

The government is also deeply interested in ensuring that relevant knowledge claims are circulated to those outside of government. U.S. Census data, for example, has become an extraordinarily widely used data source, such that virtually all quantitative studies of national-scale social and economic phenomena rely to a greater or lesser extent on Census surveys. Where once this data was provided in thick government reports, stored in U.S. government document repositories in each state, today the primary mechanism for sharing this data is the U.S. Census website, from which anyone with a computer can download the full array of Census information.

Nutritional labeling on food packaging is an even more explicit effort to ensure that knowledge claims are circulated to a wide array of citizens. Here, the goal is to significantly enhance consumer decision making by making knowledge available at the point of purchase, where consumers can compare data on different products directly with one another. As discussed above, a great deal of effort has gone into standardizing exactly what information must be provided and in what format, so that consumers can find the information easily, know what they are reading, and make use of the information. Still, questions have arisen about the effectiveness of the labels, and a new voluntary program encourages companies to make available an even simpler version of nutritional information on the front of the packages (rather than the side or rear, which is where the required labels can be found). Debates over exactly how to present nutritional information reflect deeper disagreements over the relative value of nutritional information (e.g., in comparison to corporate advertising, which is the primary content of package labels), theories of consumer information processing (e.g., how much information will a typical consumer examine before making a decision), assumptions about prior consumer knowledge (e.g., how much nutritional knowledge can the average consumer be expected to know), and the science of nutrition (e.g., is information on fats or sugars more significant for improving the healthiness of eating).

These factors are important considerations in any effort to design effective practices of knowledge circulation. Knowledge circulation must ultimately account for how to get information to relevant decision-makers, how to ensure that it arrives in a timely fashion and in a form that can be readily assimilated and used when decisions are being made, and how to ensure that users have sufficient knowledge and training to make sense of the information they are receiving.

Knowledge Application

The fourth function of knowledge systems is to put knowledge to use. As has already been discussed, for example, when constructing a new regulatory rule, the Administrator of the Environmental Protection Agency or the Food and Drug Administration will oversee a process of accumulating, sifting, and reviewing knowledge claims that might be relevant to the final decision. This will involve: internal and external processes of review of relevant scientific research and administrative hearings in which one or more presentations of relevant scientific evidence will be presented, perhaps by an agency official, perhaps by interested parties. Once this has been done, however, the agency must still decide how to put the knowledge collected and reviewed to use. This will typically entail informal and formal conversations within the agency about the available evidence, followed by an official judgment by the Administrator and a formal statement of the new rule. In the case of these two agencies, final rules will typically also be accompanied by a formal publication of the scientific evidence supporting the agency's decision in the Federal Register. Almost always, a draft rule is announced, followed by a period of public comment, then a final review by the agency before the official rule is published. Subsequently, legal suits may be brought against the agency, challenging the ruling, resulting in formal legal proceedings in which the agency's scientific reasoning may come under challenge as well.

At a far more informal level, individual consumers may also use knowledge to inform their purchasing decisions, using very different forms of knowledge uptake and processing. In our own cases, we do most of our families' shopping and use nutritional labels on food packages to limit how much sugar and fat our families eat, choosing options low in these nutrients as much as possible. We use this information to help address various health concerns, including concerns about potential future health risks from cholesterol and diabetes and food allergies. Hence, we always refer as well to ingredient lists, which now must also include bold indications of key food allergens contained in any food. We consider ourselves reasonably knowledgeable about nutrition, having read a fair bit about cholesterol, glycemic indices, food allergies, and a handful of diets. Even so, our ability to apply nutritional information remains a situation where we are unsure whether we are using information to the best possible effect. In part, this reflects limited time; conflicting theories of nutrition; and limited external expertise, metrics, and referents against which to measure our success or failure.

Knowledge application can be a complex undertaking that depends on whether the other functions of the knowledge systems are being carried out in a way that enables knowledge to be acted upon. It also depends on how the users of that knowledge perceive and trust the people and processes involved in the other functions of the knowledge system. In the following chapter, we describe some of the complexities that arise in the application of knowledge in knowledge systems, particularly in situations where there are multiple and conflicting knowledge systems interacting. We also offer ideas for how users and producers of knowledge can navigate these complexities.

Chapter 3 Takeaways

- All knowledge systems share certain general functions, which can be divided into four areas of work: knowledge generation, validation, communication, and application.

- Knowledge generation is the act of creating a knowledge claim through the process of problem formulation, data collection, data analysis, and re-porting.

- Knowledge validation consists of the practices, pro-cesses, and routines by which knowledge claims are subjected to review, critique, assessment, and so on. Common forms of knowledge validation include peer review and editorial fact-checking.

- Knowledge circulation refers to the routines, prac-tices, and processes by which knowledge claims are exchanged, transmitted, or translated. Conferences, journals, and hearings are examples of knowledge circulation.

- Knowledge application includes the social and insti-tutional practices by which knowledge is factored into decisions, also referred to as the use, uptake, or consumption of knowledge.

4

WHEN DIFFERENT WAYS OF KNOWING CONFLICT

The picture that we have described thus far has focused on the basic structures and functions of individual knowledge systems. Attending carefully to these elements can provide significant improvements to an organization's ability to manage its knowledge systems and avoid knowledge failures. But many of the challenges that confront knowledge systems also involve higher levels of complexity that stem from conflicts over different ways of knowing.[1] Even for a relatively straightforward system like the U.S. Census, in which knowledge is generated by a single organization with relatively well-defined knowledge claims, the underlying arrangements, dynamics, and politics can become significantly more complex, especially when they become embroiled in disputes with competing knowledge systems.

In this chapter, we describe some of the complexities that arise in the dynamics of knowledge systems and the ways that they come into conflict with one another and introduce ideas for making sense of when and how these kinds of complexities matters. We focus on three different forms of complexity in knowledge systems. We describe each independently, but as we illustrate in the examples, the three often interact to further complicate knowledge management and governance.

The first is organizational or structural complexity. As we described in Chapter 2, the structure of a knowledge system refers to the social and organizational arrangements, networks, and institutions involved in carrying out the core functions or tasks of a knowledge system.[2] The structures of knowledge systems can vary dramatically. In some structures, a single, well-defined organization controls the knowledge system functions: knowledge generation, validation, communication, and application. In others, these tasks may be distributed across different parts of an organization or even multiple organizations. Even if a single organization carries out these tasks, they may be accountable to other organizations with different criteria for evaluating the performance of the knowledge system.

The second factor in knowledge system complexity is operational or dynamic complexity. Operational complexity arises from the processes and routines involved in the work of knowledge systems.[3] Dynamic complexity refers both to the dynamics of operations—many moving parts, frequent interactions, shifting networks—as well as wider dynamics, such as rapidly changing conditions that require frequent readjustment. In some knowledge systems, for example, there is a clear and shared sense of the knowledge needed and the values underlying the collection of that knowledge. Moreover, the goals tend to stay consistent throughout the process (rather than frequently being retasked or reoriented), and the processes used to generate, validate, circulate, and apply the knowledge are well established, agreed upon, and tightly organized. By contrast, in more complex contexts, disagreement may exist over knowledge system values, the connection between knowledge and values may be contested, considerable work may need to be done to effectively assert the credibility of the knowledge system, or activities may need to be coordinated in complex processes and routines that don't lend themselves easily to standardization. As we describe in more detail later, we group these more complex forms of dynamic knowledge work into five types of activities: hybridization, deconstruction, boundary work, credibility performance, and orchestration.

Together, organizational and operational complexities also often contribute to the emergence of political complexity in knowledge systems, in which the work and products of knowledge systems become entangled with the exercise of power or in competition and conflict within or between organizations.[4] In modern organizations and societies, knowledge has become an essential element in how decisions get justified. It's no longer considered sufficient to simply have the power and authority to make decisions. Leaders are expected to explain their decisions, why those decisions are correct, and the evidence to support them. This inevitably involves knowledge claims and knowledge systems in the politics that surround conflicts over all sorts of decisions.

Illustrating Complexities: Two Cases

To illustrate these different forms of complexity, before diving into a more thorough analysis of each, this section explores two case studies, one national and one international.

We start with an analysis of the knowledge system that exists to inform the U.S. Food and Drug Administration (FDA) in its regulation of pharmaceutical drug markets.[5] By law, before the FDA can allow the marketing of a new pharmaceutical drug, the agency must first determine that the drug is both safe and effective. This determination must be based on scientific research and, more specifically, on research that shows via human trials that taking a drug does not create dangerous side effects and that the drug works to address a discrete medical problem. The FDA also monitors drug safety and effectiveness once a drug is on the market to determine if further evidence from ongoing use warrants subsequently removing a drug from the market.

To inform these policy judgments, the FDA has brought into being a complex knowledge system to provide scientific and other forms of evidence in support of or opposition to claims of the safety and efficacy of drugs. This knowledge system is organizationally complex in that it involves complex relationships among multiple organizations. For example, the functions of the knowledge system are distributed across a variety of organizations, including the FDA itself (which sets standards of quality for drug research, funds some research, reviews evidence, and applies it), as well as pharmaceutical companies (which sponsor and conduct research) and universities (which also conduct research, review and validate it, and synthesize and review evidence in peer-reviewed publications).

Research contributing to FDA regulation is usually generated, first and foremost, by the company that intends to market the drug, but also potentially by independent research institutions such as universities. Knowledge validation is also shared across several organizations: the institution conducting the research does some validation; additional validation is carried out through scientific journal peer review processes; and the FDA independently evaluates data and research in its own processes. Knowledge application is typically done by multiple groups, including the manufacturing company, patient activist groups, university researchers, and others, each of which is invited to present their interpretation of the relevant data and its implications for regulation to the FDA advisory panel. The FDA advisory panel then does its own application work and makes a recommendation to the FDA administrator, who determines and issues the final regulatory decision.

Operationally, the FDA knowledge system is also complex. While the key values of the system are well established (drugs must be safe and effective), balancing between the two can be difficult, and their evaluation may be different for different populations (children, adults, and the elderly, for instance). The administration of the system requires extensive coordination of complex routines and procedures, including standardizing research protocols, coordinating research across many institutions, organizing testimony from diverse and often competing groups, and adjudicating among their different interpretations of the meaning and significance of data and analyses. Similarly, the collection, synthesis, analysis, and implantation of decisions based on knowledge generated by the FDA's side effect monitoring program requires careful coordination, not least because it depends on millions of doctors and other health care practitioners to effectively and efficiently report health outcomes data for users of new drugs.

Finally, the system is politically complex. The FDA's organizational and operational complexities can give rise to extensive political conflict. The regulatory implications of the agency's decisions are enormous, as are the potential health impacts (good and bad) of new drugs. The FDA's core activity involves a significant exercise of government power to intervene in and regulate markets, and the core purpose of the FDA's knowledge system is to inform and justify that exercise of power. Thus the FDA's knowledge system is inherently involved in political conflicts — and, indeed, many facets of the knowledge system have been legislated by Congress. Both the FDA and the companies that it regulates can also be taken to court by individuals or groups that desire to challenge their decisions — another process that guarantees frequent and extensive social and political conflict surrounding not only drug use, manufacturing, and marketing, but the evidentiary basis on which regulatory decisions get made.

Climate change offers a second illustration of knowledge system complexity. As we observed earlier, climate change has become the subject of a vast and complex knowledge system.[6] The world's governments have collectively spent approximately $4 billion per year on climate research since 1990. By itself, the United States has spent roughly $50 billion over the past quarter century to put satellites into space that can observe the Earth's climate and to build the world's largest and most complex computer models to predict how the climate will change under different scenarios of future carbon dioxide emissions.[7]

Organizationally, the climate knowledge system is highly complex. Even if we limit discussion to the conduct of climate research, thousands of organizations are involved, including numerous different kinds of organizations (e.g., national laboratories, universities, private research facilities, etc.) across hundreds of countries. Participants have been trained in dozens of disciplinary traditions and, as studies of the climate knowledge system have shown, disagree over even such basic questions as how best to design and interpret the results of models of the global climate.[8] Over the years, numerous other organizations have also become involved in efforts to makes sense of how to translate climate research into meaningful insights about what climate change will mean for human affairs on scales from the globe down to individual communities, organizations, and places. These organizations include government agencies, think tanks, advocacy organizations, local communities, and even individuals and families. This highly distributed arrangement of knowledge generation, validation, circulation, and application is highly complex and makes extremely difficult, for example, efforts to develop and implement coordinated programs of climate adaptation on regional or national scales.

Operationally, many parts of the climate knowledge system are, by themselves, relatively straightforward in operation. Many individual research laboratories, for example, have a relatively narrow scope of focus, are organized around one or a small number of principal investigators and their teams, and typically limit their work to the generation of a specific kind of knowledge. Other facets of the climate knowledge system are more complex, however. One example is the work of the Intergovernmental Panel on Climate Change (IPCC).[9] Every five years, under the auspices of the IPCC, thousands of scientists from all over the world spend hundreds of thousands of hours reviewing and synthesizing the output of climate research, preparing a global assessment of the state of the Earth's climate, and subjecting that assessment to thorough review by many other scientists and government and industry experts. The result is a multi-volume document designed to provide policy officials with the most accurate and up to date version of another relatively simple knowledge claim: The Earth's climate is changing due to the buildup of carbon dioxide in the atmosphere caused by human activities.

The work of the IPCC is highly complex, operationally, with numerous dynamic and interactive elements that require extensive coordination and management.[10] The organization is split between a plenary body, comprising representatives of member governments, and three scientific working groups, which involve scientists from all over the planet. The working groups define the chapters to be written and select lead authors (who in turn select author teams), always paying careful attention not only to the knowledge of participants but also the desire to create diverse and representative teams (most chapter teams, for example, strive for multiple authors from countries that are geographically and socio-economically diverse). Once the teams have drafted chapters, they are sent out for review by scientists and governments, whose comments are collected and responded to by the author teams. Those responses are subsequently evaluated by a review editor who ensures that authors have properly addressed review comments. Summaries are then drafted for each working group, and the final document is then reviewed by the plenary, which accepts chapters but line-by-line negotiates the wording of the summaries.

The operational complexity of the IPCC results, in part, from the magnitude of the data and research to be reviewed and the number and diversity of people and countries wanting to be involved. But it also stems, in part, from the fact that the IPCC's work is politically sensitive, significant, and frequently contentious.[11] The IPCC was created by governments to provide sanctioned scientific input into the negotiation of international treaties, and the precise wording of its key conclusions matters enormously to governments. This significance is both instrumental—meaning that it influences what governments do—and highly symbolic. Not surprisingly, the IPCC has become a lightning rod for opponents of climate policies. On multiple occasions, outside groups opposed to strong action on climate change have criticized the IPCC. This criticism has often focused not only on the knowledge synthesized by the IPCC and the proposed actions that result, but also on whether IPCC participants have followed the organization's complex rules of operation.[12] Not surprisingly, the IPCC response has frequently been to create even more layers of rules and procedures for author teams and reviewers to follow (in turn creating more opportunities for failing to properly implement the expanded rules). At other times, national governments have lambasted IPCC author teams for what they viewed as faulty assumptions embedded in IPCC chapters. India, for example, has expressed significant skepticism on several occasions of the assumptions made by IPCC economists about how to calculate the value of lives lost due to climate change in efforts to measure the net impacts of climate change.[13]

More generally, the climate knowledge system has been the subject of deep political conflict. As we will describe in more detail later in the chapter, contemporary politics often substitutes conflict and competition over knowledge for other forms of political conflict and competition. This has certainly been the case for climate change, particularly in the United States, where diverse political groups have recruited members of the scientific community to represent them in disputes over the reliability, validity, and implications of everything from individual scientific studies to the work of the IPCC. In one notable move, for example, the George W. Bush Administration criticized the IPCC for presenting a "United Nations" and, by implication, therefore, not American, perspective on climate change. They then ostentatiously asked the U.S. National Academy of Sciences to review the then most recent IPCC report, expecting a critical assessment. The move backfired, however, when the National Academy not only largely supported the IPCC's conclusions but also observed that over half of the participants in the IPCC work were U.S. scientists. The National Academy report dealt the Bush Administration a serious political defeat.

In the rest of this chapter, we describe in more detail the concepts of organizational, operational, and political complexity.

Organizational Complexity

Most discussions of knowledge and decision making adopt something close to the simplest possible model of a knowledge system as their starting point. As a result, most discussions of knowledge systems radically oversimplify the process of making and using knowledge. This simplistic model looks something like this:

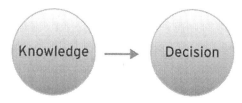

Figure 1. The relationship between knowledge and decision-making is often incorrectly assumed to be a one-way flow of information from knowledge holders to decision makers.[14]

The idea that decisions would be better if we could just speak truth to power—if we could just get the right information to the right people—is remarkably widespread. This idea posits that some people have knowledge and others just need to be exposed to that knowledge to make better decisions. Unfortunately, the problem is rarely that easy, as the cases of nutritional labeling and greenhouse gas emissions inventories described in Chapters 2 and 3 suggest. Knowing what information people need is not always straightforward. They may misinterpret what they're being told. They may be presented with alternative information from other sources. The knowledge may not arrive in a timely fashion. It may not be salient to their decisions. Uncertainties may not be properly accounted for. And so forth.

Moving one step up the ladder of complexity involves recognizing that rarely do we just have knowledge and decisions. Rather, as we have described in earlier chapters, knowledge systems involve processes of knowledge making and decision making. Knowledge gets generated, validated, circulated, and applied to decisions through a variety of social and institutional routines and practices. At the same time, decision making also occurs through a suite of social and institutional routines and practices. For the sake of simplicity, we often say that the leader of an organization or community makes the decision, but even when that is a reasonable approximation of what happens, the contours of that decision are thoroughly shaped by the options presented to the leader, the opinions of others in the organization that matter, etc. And, often, the leader doesn't make a lone decision at all. Rather, decisions are made in complex decision-making landscapes that involve vertically and horizontally distributed decision-making authority, a multiplicity of interacting actors and viewpoints, and complicated rules of procedure. Not surprisingly, we find processes and arrangements of knowledge making and decision making interact in complex, bi-directional ways.[15]

Figure 2. Knowledge-making and decision-making routinely influence one another in a bi-directional relationship, creating tight linkages between how knowledge gets made and used.

Indeed, where the relationship between knowledge making and decision making works well (which is to say, where knowledge claims are used to good effect in making decisions that then have arguably good outcomes), there are typically dynamic links that closely tie the social practices of knowledge making to the social practices of decision making. This may be direct, such as when Congress asks the National Academy of Sciences to produce a specific report addressing specific questions. Or it may be indirect, like when a knowledge producer and decision maker have both been trained in the same methods and problem-orientation. In either case, certain forms of knowledge making and decision making become tightly interwoven with one another. This is especially true where decision making is routinized or bureaucratic, but remains true even where it is not.

This kind of tight coupling between knowledge and decision making evolves over time in many knowledge systems.[16] This feedback happens in both directions. Feedback from decision-makers causes the groups making knowledge claims to tweak their processes. These tweaks alter the content of knowledge claims, or how they are presented, just enough (e.g., by reducing their uncertainty or focusing attention on a different but closely related variable) that decision-makers start to pay more attention and grant them greater credibility. Other changes may happen in how knowledge is framed[17] or in the timing and frequency of knowledge-making processes. Such changes can happen in response to a specific request, because advocacy groups time their activities to the dynamics of decision-making processes, or because administrative processes create incentives to align knowledge to decision making. Corporate and public sector accounting systems, for example, are set up explicitly to feed into periodic processes for determining the allocation of budgets across different departments or agencies. As much as possible, accounting knowledge systems are organized to provide exactly the right information to the right people to make good budget decisions. When they don't do so, organizations can get into serious budgetary and even legal problems.

At the same time, decision-making procedures also evolve over time to fit knowledge that is available from knowledge systems. Historically, for example, the cost of data generation has been extremely high for public agencies. Consequently, agencies have often relied on existing knowledge systems rather than try to create new ones. An illuminating illustration of this occurred in the case of local sustainability indicator programs in the 1990s. In these programs, local communities sought to supplement traditional metrics of local development (and, especially, economic development) with a wider array of measures of the sustainability of local policy actions. Through various community engagement processes, local leaders often developed rich and robust ideas of what sustainability meant to their constituents. Often, however, they didn't have direct measures of sustainability outcomes and, thus, were forced to fall back on an array of already measured data. The cost of creating new data sets was simply too expensive, in many cases, for local governments to imagine pursuing.

As we illustrate in the figure below, when knowledge-making and decision-making processes and arrangements become tightly coupled to one another, integrating new knowledge into this form of closed system can be a very difficult undertaking. If the four tasks of knowledge systems — knowledge generation, validation, circulation, and application — are working in sync, they evolve tightly coupled feedback loops that ensure that specific kinds of knowledge are created, reviewed for common errors, made available to decision-makers at precisely the right time and in a compelling way, and used to good effect. Because these systems can be so tightly coupled, re-opening knowledge systems to allow new forms of knowledge to enter the decision-making process is critical, but can be quite difficult.

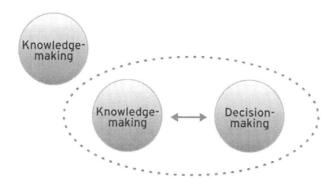

Figure 3. Bringing new knowledge into an existing decision-making context often requires reconfiguring the social and epistemic practices in place that tightly couple the making and use of knowledge in a prior knowledge system.

Proponents of the protection of endangered species have faced this challenge directly. Consider, for example, efforts to discourage restaurant customers from eating endangered fish.[18] When ordering off a menu, most people derive the knowledge they use from their own experiences (what they like to eat, what the restaurant is known for, or what have they had before), the server (what's the special, what's good today), and the menu (what's offered, how much does it cost). Getting even environmentally minded people to stop and think about whether a fish is endangered or has been caught sustainably turns out to be very hard. Generating and validating information on fish species and, more importantly, on the fish purchased by the restaurant is difficult enough. Getting that information to customers is also difficult, as is getting them to act on that information.

Some groups have adopted cards that a person can put in their wallet and carry with them. This does not allow for change over time, however, nor do people necessarily always take the card out and look at it (peer pressure may mitigate against this when, for instance, going out with a client or the boss). The restaurant may use a different name than is found on the card. Another approach might be to get the restaurant to put the information on the menu, but this may be unreliable, unless the chef and owner could be convinced to serve only sustainably harvested fish. Even if the restaurant decided to purchase only sustainably harvested fish, they'd still need a purchaser who knew of the request and could reliably supply the fish (instead of, for instance, a different species intentionally being passed off as more expensive fish). Moreover, a series of values questions would be introduced, such as whether it was preferable to serve farmed fish or wild-caught fish. Introducing sustainability information when shopping for household goods has many of the same problems.

The challenge of eating — let alone promoting — sustainably harvested fish illustrates the full organizational complexity of many knowledge systems. Rather than a simple case of knowledge informing a decision, advocates of sustainable fisheries face a complex web of multiple arenas of knowledge making and decision making, including among fishermen, regulatory agencies, scientists, designers of fishing equipment, groceries, restaurants, and consumers. Each of these groups operates their own tightly coupled knowledge and decision-making arrangements and processes that are, at a higher level of organization, also intertwined with one another. Achieving sustainable outcomes for fisheries entails reconfiguring this whole complex institutional and epistemic landscape.

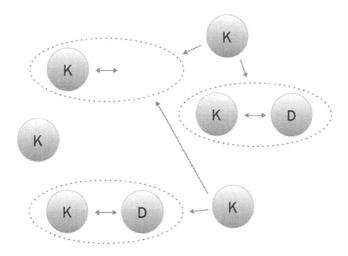

Figure 4. Contemporary decision-making landscapes regularly entail complex relationships and dynamics between many knowers and deciders, and thus many knowledge-making and decision-making processes.[19]

Another example of this complexity can be seen in the challenge of managing ecosystems using the concept of ecosystem services. The idea of ecosystem services is that any given ecosystem provides services to humans and that changes to the ecosystem will create changes to the services provided. For example, forests provide an array of ecosystem services, such as sustainably harvested forest products, wildlife viewing opportunities, some water quality improvement, and so forth. Or forests may be converted for agricultural use, which provides a different set of ecosystem services (enhanced production of food or fiber, but loss of soil nutrients).

Management decisions involving ecosystem services thus typically involve a decision about how to trade off one set of ecosystem services against another. From the perspective of reasoned decision making, trade-offs present a difficult knowledge problem. Knowledge of the trade-offs among ecosystem services is often absent from or neglected within existing decision-making processes, leading to decisions that have unexpected or problematic outcomes.[20] As we mentioned before, solving the problem of finding ways to reconfigure knowledge making and decision making across complex social networks is therefore a critical problem. At the same time, trade-offs among ecosystem services highlight the complexity of knowledge systems stemming from the fact that they typically involve multiple social contexts of both decision making and knowledge making.[21] Typically, such decisions involve multiple decision-makers. When deciding whether to convert land from forest to agriculture, it may be that many individual land owners are involved or that a natural park owned by the government nonetheless also has individuals who (legally or illegally) use part of the forest for various purposes.[22] Or it may be that in a democratic society, environmental NGOs, farm cooperatives, large agribusinesses, and indigenous communities all feel they have a stake in the decision about how to conserve the land.

Similarly, decisions involving trade-offs often involve multiple knowledge claims arising from diverse processes of knowledge generation and review that need to be bridged, integrated, or engaged in knowledge-making and decision-making processes.[23] Two scientific studies of the potential agricultural value of the land may arrive at very different estimates of its long-term productivity. Indigenous communities may hold knowledge of the forest and its ecosystem services that isn't contained in scientific research. And different groups may diverge in how they interpret and judge the resulting evidence and uncertainty, thus giving rise to different conclusions about what claims should be valued and applied to decisions. It is highly common in such settings to observe these kinds of conflicts over knowledge and its meaning or value for a particular choice.

Here we see clearly the challenge of shifting from a problem of policy optimization (which often assumes a single decision-maker) to more complex problems of multistakeholder governance.[24] Once it is clear that multiple forms of knowledge and multiple decision-makers are present, the requirements for knowledge systems alter dramatically.[25]

Even a relatively simple case of two groups and two potential ecosystem services, where the two groups must agree on a collective solution through bargaining and/or persuasion, poses complex challenges. Here, there are several possible approaches to knowledge system design. One might, as was the case with the U.S. Office of Technology Assessment, create a neutral organization that sought very carefully to develop an objective body of evidence that would fully outline the various trade-offs available, so that the bargaining could occur based on the best possible overall knowledge.[26] Or, one might, as is often the case in U.S. legal settings or adversarial politics, provide both groups with sufficient funding to establish their own knowledge system. In this latter case, one is likely to get studies that are more clearly skewed toward one side or the other, but long experience has shown that such an arrangement is also often more likely to bring to light hidden aspects of the underlying trade-off problem that a neutral knowledge system might miss.[27] One reason for the difference is that the objectively neutral knowledge-maker is often constrained in how widely it can pursue questions that would result in the appearance of bias from one side or the other. This limitation is less constraining for more independent knowledge agents. More generally, the challenge can be understood as one of deciding where and how to consider trade-offs within the knowledge system. Is the goal of the system simply to highlight trade-offs for decision-makers, or is it to conduct analyses that help resolve trade-offs? Or is it to highlight the unique trade-offs that face multiple knowledge holders and decision-makers within a particular conservation context? Or is the goal something else entirely? The answers to these questions are often situational and demand careful consideration from knowledge professionals and the organizations they work for.

Operational Complexity

The second element of knowledge system complexity involves the necessity of complex knowledge work: the social work involved in carrying out the core functions of knowledge systems (knowledge generation, validation, circulation, and application) is highly dynamic, involves diverse participants, and requires careful coordination across the system's many organizational components. The literature examining the social organization and dynamics of knowledge work is one of the most rapidly growing fields of social science — known under various titles from the sociology of science or scientific knowledge to science and technology studies. This literature provides a wealth of insights and information to the patient reader.

To help make sense of operational complexity, we have developed a framework that describes five different types of knowledge work that knowledge systems do: hybridization, deconstruction, boundary work, credibility performance, and orchestration.[28]

- **Hybridization** refers to the synthesis of diverse kinds of knowledge claims with diverse values to create fact-value hybrids. We described this kind of work in Chapters 2 and 3 in talk about how facts and values are combined to create meaningful knowledge claims.

- **Deconstruction** is the reverse of hybridization: the dismantling of hybrids into fact-claims and value-claims, to create transparency and allow the possibility to recombine and reconfigure hybrids in new forms.

- **Boundary work** is the capacity to appropriately delineate, operationalize, maintain, dissolve, and represent boundaries between different kinds of knowledge work occurring within knowledge systems, and especially between scientific work and other kinds of work (politics, law, ethics, etc.).

- **Credibility performance** relates to the actions that a knowledge system must take to ensure that its generation, review, circulation, and application of knowledge claims are viewed as credible or believable by diverse audiences.

- **Orchestration** is the capacity to coordinate the work of diverse parts of the knowledge system to enable the whole to work well.

In this way of grouping knowledge work, the central element is the hybridization or weaving together of facts and values to produce a knowledge claim. While conventional approaches often treat knowledge solely in terms of facts, as we discussed earlier, knowledge claims are generally hybrids that blend facts and value choices. Inside an existing knowledge system, like the Census, these value choices may be taken for granted and so not given much attention. When analyzing knowledge systems operations, however, understanding how values get interwoven into knowledge claims is crucial.

In Chapter 2, for example, we described at length various aspects of hybridization in the effort to define and measure pollutant emissions for environmental policymaking, usually called an emissions inventory. Emissions inventories must not only measure how much of each pollutant is emitted into the atmosphere, they must, at the same time, define which emissions to count and allocate those emissions to responsible parties. Accomplishing these tasks necessarily involves welding facts and values. Deciding how to weld facts and values appropriately and then conducting the work to do so is an example of hybridization. In the case of determining responsibility for climate change under the United Nations Framework Convention on Climate Change (UNFCCC) that we described in Chapter 2, the knowledge system measures and allocates emissions of greenhouse gases but not other causes of climate change, such as changes in the Earth's albedo. It measures and allocates those emissions to countries, not to individuals or to companies. It also determines which methodologies are acceptable and which are not for measuring emissions. All of this involves the integration of claims about the state of the world (e.g., estimates of how many greenhouse gases are being emitted, from what processes, where in the world) with value commitments (e.g., about the kinds of entities that bear responsibility under international treaties). As we also discussed in Chapters 2 and 3, it also involves processes of simplification (e.g., of complex data sets and/or the features of the world they represent) and specification (of how to apply general principles to specific cases) at work in a knowledge system that also bring value judgments of a different kind to bear on knowledge making.

The second facet of knowledge work is deconstruction, which is the reverse of hybridization. Deconstruction refers to the activities and practices of knowledge systems that enable the taking apart of hybrid knowledge claims to reflect systematically on their underlying knowledge and value dimensions. In the case of greenhouse gas emissions inventories, for example, each country's inventory is subjected to a formal review process under the UNFCCC. These reviews are designed to reveal aspects of the inventory that independent experts from other countries believe can be improved, and they generally involve extensive deconstruction work by the reviewing experts.

Many knowledge systems use peer review mechanisms of one sort or another for precisely this purpose. Others create processes — or are part of larger organizational or societal cultures that encourage equivalent dynamics — by which different groups can gain access to, evaluate, and interpret knowledge claims using their own criteria, facilitating the development of clashes of competing or conflicting perspectives on what the right strategy for hybridizing facts and values should be. In the U.S. legal system, for example, both parties to a trial are allowed access to key knowledge claims — such as evidence of the commission of a crime — in order to ensure they can subject it to independent review and analysis.[29]

One of the purposes of deconstruction is to allow determination of the precise fact-value composition of the knowledge claim. Many times, it is crucial to be able to determine what forms of simplification and specification have taken place, the extent of different kinds of technical uncertainties that exist, or the tacit assumptions that were embedded in the construction of a knowledge claim to evaluate its relevance to a particular application or decision. The transparency of knowledge claims can also be significant politically, in enabling a robust deliberation of what a knowledge claim means and how to effectively put it to use.[30]

A final purpose of deconstruction is to facilitate re-hybridization: the deliberate reconfiguration of the factual and/or value elements of a claim to adjust it to fit better into new contexts or purposes. One particularly common problem for knowledge generation occurs when knowledge claims are moved from one application to another without significant evaluation of whether, in both fact and value terms, they fit well into the new application. For example, many times, regulators seek to apply a model that had been designed to work in one country to the same problem in another country. Unfortunately, in our experience, this is often done without delving sufficiently into the details of the modeling work and translating it to work effectively. Such modeling work is often expensive. But there may be many facets of the model—e.g., its assumptions about geographic or socio-economic variables, regulatory standards, tolerance of uncertainty—that are no longer appropriate for the new conditions. Taking the model apart, via deconstruction, to reveal those assumptions and enable them to be changed, can significantly improve the model's performance and reduce the likelihood of knowledge failures.

The third facet of knowledge work is boundary work.[31] As we discussed earlier, the boundaries of knowledge systems are almost always fluid and flexible, both around the edges of the system (i.e., what's in and what's out) and internally between different kinds of activities within the work of the system. Boundary work is the work of trying to make the boundaries of and within knowledge systems clearer and sharper, whether operationally or in appearance. There are two particularly common examples of boundary work in knowledge systems. One is to differentiate scientific or technical work from political or values-oriented work within the system, as is illustrated so well by the work of Sheila Jasanoff on the politics of science advice in federal regulatory agencies.[32] Most knowledge systems operate on at least a tacit (and often explicit) presumption that the technical work of the system should be handled independently by different parts of the system and using different rules and procedures from more clearly value-laden work. In practice, this is impossible to maintain strictly, but it is often seen as desirable to uphold at least an appearance of separation, necessitating boundary work.

The other most common form of boundary work is to differentiate the work of the knowledge system from other knowledge systems, again, often for the purposes of shoring up the credibility of the system.[33] In practice, any kind of differentiation of activity may be subject to boundary work. Disciplines may seek to bound off different aspects of a problem. In energy, for instance, engineers often see their work as focusing only on the technology, while economists assess the costs of those technologies once designed. Similarly, different organizations or parts of an organization may seek to draw boundaries between different facets of the system's operation, as in the frequent desire to separate the generation of knowledge from its application. The fear is that introducing values or requirements from the application context may distort the knowledge created, but creating too high of a boundary between the two can also create problems where the knowledge created no longer meets the needs of users.

Boundary work is carried out in language, in practice, and in organizational design. A key element of boundary work is people talking about and arguing for the need to separate different domains of activity. Scientists and politicians, for example, frequently support the idea that "science should inform but not make policy." This phrase illustrates an example of boundary work in asserting that science and policy are different domains of activity and that they should remain separate to be legitimate. If science becomes too activist, it might distort its knowledge claims, so the argument goes; and if policy gets made by scientists instead of elected leaders, democracy suffers. Boundary work can also be found in practice and organization, with different institutions or different parts of an institution separated off and isolated from one another by physical, virtual, or procedural distance.

Despite the regular performance of boundary work, efforts at complete separation will always fall short. Because knowledge claims are hybrids of values and facts, one can never actually accomplish a clean differentiation of domains. Bits and pieces of any given domain always end up migrating across domains. Thus, boundary work inevitably entails the creation of illusion, or what the sociologist of science Stephen Hilgartner calls stagecraft, by managing expectations and appearances.[34] In this sense, boundary work serves at least two critical purposes in knowledge production. The first is establishing the authority of expertise within the knowledge system. Most cultures today operate with a deep, historically established conviction that the authoritative forms of expertise are those that are independent of social and political influence and values. The force of this conviction is reinforced—and made real, in some sense—through ongoing boundary work to separate scientific work from the work of other realms like law, politics, and religion. That said, science is not the only authority established through boundary work, as professions like the law and medicine also use boundary-differentiating strategies to construct their own authority. Likewise, indigenous groups have used boundary work to establish authority for their knowledge and political claims.

The second reason many conduct boundary work is for its importance to the performance of credibility within the knowledge system.[35] Credibility is the idea that a person or organization is believable when they make a knowledge claim. Contrary to conventional belief, the credibility of experts and of knowledge claims generally does not flow from the unassailable truth of knowledge. Rather, credibility is the outcome of social processes and practices of negotiation and contestation. Much boundary work—and the deconstruction of boundaries, which also occurs frequently in contexts in which knowledge claims are contested—is designed to help shore up or weaken credibility. But the establishment and performance of credibility also involves a wide variety of additional considerations beyond boundary work, including credentials, demonstrations of skill or veracity, historical record of truthfulness, and many more.[36]

The metaphor of stagecraft, mentioned above, is a powerful one — and why we choose to call this aspect of knowledge work a performance, although it could also be called credibility management. Credibility (or its absence) is most often at stake in what Steven Epstein, who studies the politics of knowledge, has called credibility contests, in which diverse groups argue over whose knowledge claims should be given greatest credence in making key decisions and deploy various resources to shore up their own credibility (and the credibility of their knowledge claims) and weaken those of their opponents.[37] Credibility, historian and sociologist of science Steven Shapin has suggested, is always simultaneously about people and their claims. Knowledge claims never stand by themselves. They always come attached to the credibility of the people or organizations that make them. In Shakespeare's *King Lear*, Cordelia's protestations of her love fall short not because they're not true — she does indeed love her father — but because he doesn't believe her.[38]

The final aspect of knowledge work is orchestration. Since knowledge systems almost always engage in boundary work of some form, setting up discrete domains of activity, and since those domains inevitably leak at the boundaries, knowledge systems must manage and orchestrate work across these bounded domains. When a suggestion is made, for example, about how to improve a knowledge system (see the next chapter), the system must be able to reflect carefully on which domains need to evaluate the proposed improvement and how to integrate the various evaluations and determine whether to adopt the proposal.

More generally, examining the dynamics and practices of boundary work and orchestration within a knowledge system is crucial to understanding how the politics of expertise play out within the system. Particularly, examining how expertise is distributed across the system—in terms of which actors have credibility and authority, and who gets to decide what—reveals how power dynamics work in the production, sharing, and use of policy-relevant knowledge. This, in turn, gives an indication of who is taken seriously (and who is not), and hence, what expertise is being privileged in the planning and decision-making process.[39] This knowledge is also useful to developing capacities for governance. It contributes understanding of which organizational and institutional arrangements are more conducive to explicitly integrating multiple expertise and politics in the planning and policy process in order to be more effective at resolving complex controversies.

Political Complexity

Political complexity arises because knowledge systems—and the creation, validation, communication, and application of knowledge within them—are often deeply intertwined with the use of power.[40] The relationship between knowledge and power is bi-directional: (1) power shapes the organization and control of knowledge systems, their design, and their operations; and (2) knowledge systems and their knowledge claims shape the making and justification of decisions to use power. Those who wield power often do so to shape what others know—recall George Orwell's *1984* and the efforts of the state to prevent people from even thinking things the state didn't want them to think about. At the same time, the ability to produce knowledge can be a powerful route to influence decisions.

The dynamic interactions between knowledge and power often lead to two very different outcomes. On the one hand, the making of knowledge and decisions can become closely aligned and integrated over time, creating monopolies over knowledge and power that reinforce one another and shore up one another's influence and significance.[41] Such alignments often routinize forms of knowledge making in support of particular approaches to decision making, where the two together prevent other forms of knowledge and other approaches to decision making from gaining any purchase. On the other hand, the significance of knowledge in justifying the exercise of power can create incentives for multiple, diverse groups in society to invest heavily in their own knowledge systems, with the result that knowledge making becomes highly contested, especially in political cultures like the United States that foster and catalyze political competition.[42]

The evolution of science and expert advice within U.S. federal government decision making offers a more dynamic illustration of the rise of political complexity in knowledge systems. Beginning in the Progressive Era, federal agencies like the U.S. Forest Service, Bureau of Land Management, and Bureau of Reclamation began to hire significant numbers of experts to manage natural resources. This effort, justified in terms of the rationalization of resource use for the national good, created the rise of expert bureaucracies and, as historian Samuel Hays has described in detail, contributed to a significant shift in power toward the federal government and away from the states.[43] At the same time, within the federal government, the Presidency acquired significant new power in relation to Congress, which increasingly ceded rule-making authority to the new agencies, and to the Courts, which largely deferred to agency expertise on the content of regulatory rules.[44]

Over time, the growth in the power of the federal bureaucracy led to a variety of efforts to put checks on the power of expert knowledge aligned with the decision-making authority of the executive branch. In the 1930s and

1940s, for example, Congress increasingly insisted on the development of standardized forms of knowledge making, such as cost-benefit analysis, that would constrain the discretion of federal agencies by forcing them to justify their decisions on well-defined grounds.[45] In the 1970s, Congress turned to two additional approaches to placing limits on the power of agency science. In setting up new federal agencies, like the Environmental Protection Administration, and reforming others, like the FDA, Congress both required these agencies to justify new federal rules with clear scientific evidence and created external scientific advisory boards with considerable power to review, assess, and criticize the scientific work carried out by agency experts.[46] At the same time, via the Federal Advisory Committee Act, Congress standardized and regulated the use of expert advisory committees, which had become another source of power for the Executive Branch. Also in the 1970s, the U.S. Supreme Court moved to rebalance the authority of federal courts with respect to federal agencies through what came to be termed the "Hard Look Doctrine," which encouraged courts to actively review agency decisions not only on procedural grounds (which is typical for the U.S. legal system) but also on agency judgments of expertise (which is far rarer).[47]

Combined with the norms of the 1946 Administrative Procedures Act, which required the use of administrative hearings to allow multiple parties to present evidence on agency rule-making, these developments in the politics of federal expertise contributed to a political environment in which knowledge making became a central focus of regulatory rule making. As a result, parties with significant interest in federal rule making came to recognize the importance of knowledge as a political tool and, as a result, invested heavily in scientific research capabilities and other knowledge-making capacities in order to be able to support or contest agency expertise. Such parties included both industry groups and activist organizations, and other entities with significant research capacities also became embroiled in the new knowledge politics, including universities. Increasingly, through the late 1970s, 1980s, and 1990s, these organizations competed with one another in administrative hearings, scientific journals, and the media to assert the credibility of their knowledge claims and to denigrate those of their opponents.[48]

Not surprisingly, the last few decades of the 20th century were fraught with deep conflicts over knowledge in U.S. politics. Up through the 1980s, for example, the Food and Drug Administration's regulation of the marketing and availability of new drugs in the United States went mostly unchallenged, and the FDA adopted a standardized methodology for producing knowledge to be used in evaluating new drugs for safety and efficacy. As Steven Epstein described in his book *Impure Science*, the FDA's monopoly was ultimately challenged by a coalition of activist movements, led predominantly by AIDS activists, who were able to simultaneously challenge key values of the FDA knowledge system (with the aim of receiving much earlier access to experimental drugs) while allying with a group of biostatisticians to challenge the FDA's epistemology (allowing for drug trials to be expanded to much more diverse populations of participants while still generating relevant knowledge for regulatory decision making).[49]

Nor has the FDA been alone in experiencing knowledge conflicts. The knowledge claims underpinning Environmental Protection Agency (EPA) regulatory decisions have been widely contested by both industry groups and environmental organizations, depending on which group perceived an interest in undermining EPA credibility on any given policy issue. As science and technology scholar Sheila Jasanoff's research has shown, the presence of the EPA Science Advisory Board served in many cases to exacerbate knowledge conflicts rather than mitigate them by presenting another opportunity for divergent views of the proper use of scientific evidence to arise and become subject to critical commentary by policy actors.[50] Throughout this period, the EPA suffered long, protracted conflicts over regulatory science and its application to rule-making in political fights over asbestos, Agent Orange, silicone breast implants, etc. Similar high profile battles have been fought by federal agencies over the evidentiary basis for determining that tobacco was a health hazard and that climate change was a significant environmental risk.

Conclusion

In this chapter, we outlined ideas for grappling with the complexities of knowledge systems, especially where they grow to incorporate multiple dynamic elements or to encompass diverse ways of producing, vetting, communicating, and consuming knowledge that can come into conflict with one another. Effectively managing these complexities is one of the most difficult tasks of knowledge professionals but also one of the most important for handling the politics of knowledge and preventing significant knowledge failures. In the next chapter, we look at how organizations and knowledge professionals can begin to put some of the ideas and tools of knowledge systems analysis into practice to develop their capabilities to be knowledge-aware and to avoid the kind of knowledge failures we have discussed throughout the book.

Chapter 4 Takeaways

- Three forms of complexity in knowledge systems are organizational or structural complexity, operational or dynamic complexity, and political complexity.

- Organizational complexity is the result of decision-making landscapes that involve vertically and horizontally distributed decision-making authority, a multiplicity of interacting actors and viewpoints, and complicated rules of procedure.

- Operational complexity involves the social work involved in carrying out the core functions of knowledge systems (knowledge generation, validation, circulation, and application), and includes hybridization, deconstruction, boundary work, credibility performance, and orchestration.

- Political complexity arises because knowledge systems are often deeply intertwined with the use of power, which has a bi-directional relationship with knowledge.

5

CREATING A KNOWLEDGE-AWARE ORGANIZATION

Read any number of routine reports on the performance of large corporations or newer, smaller business ventures and two insights emerge about those who are responsible for creating, maintaining, and evolving knowledge systems. The first is that a growing number of high-profile leaders and organizations recognize the significance of knowledge systems. We agree. We have argued throughout this book that knowledge systems are essential for making good decisions. Nonetheless, it is significant, we believe, that many organizations are beginning to identify knowledge systems as strategic assets and to give greater attention to how their knowledge systems work. Leaders of some of the most successful businesses in the world attribute their success to how they acquire knowledge and to the knowledge professionals who can help them better understand those systems.

The second lesson is less optimistic: existing organizational knowledge systems are not good enough. Business publications, such as a recent article in *Business 2.0*, celebrate the ability of leaders to supplement or get around their organization's primary knowledge systems with alternative ways of generating and communicating knowledge. In that *Business 2.0* article, the CEO of a medical technology firm only discovered that his customers were angry with his company's products when he visited a surgeon himself. A consumer products company didn't have a system in place, initially, that would alert senior management to patterns of local problems in the supply chain. R&D scientists and engineers at another company were apparently not reaching outside of their own labs—either to others in the company, e.g., in marketing, or to outside experts—for the new ideas and insights that would stimulate new innovations. Many companies seem to be failing to take advantage of the knowledge and expertise of their workforce to improve operations. In perhaps the starkest example, one company became so distrustful of the knowledge presented by their mergers and acquisitions team that they developed a second team to conduct robust counter-analyses of proposed deals, thus helping them avoid costly mistakes.

Not only do these examples suggest a lack of conviction in conventional business knowledge systems, they highlight that many organizations lack both an understanding of how existing knowledge systems work (or don't work) and the knowledge systems professionals who could help them. Each of the business leaders interviewed for the *Business 2.0* feature offered up one interesting innovation in knowledge acquisition. Yet not one recommended a thorough analysis and assessment of business knowledge systems to make sure the organizations knows exactly what it needs. There may be many reasons for this, but it suggests that, even as business leaders recognize the importance of knowledge systems, the organizations that they lead are neither in full command of their knowledge systems nor necessarily even recognize them for what they are.

These observations buttress our conclusion that a new focus on knowledge systems and knowledge systems professionals is sorely needed in today's organizations. In this final chapter, we offer some thoughts on how the ideas presented throughout this book can be put into practice to address these challenges. These recommendations will help to build a knowledge-aware organization—i.e., an organization whose employees and leaders recognize the significance of their knowledge systems, are aware of their strengths and limitations, and can respond appropriately when those systems encounter new circumstances that threaten their reliability.

A knowledge-aware organization, for us, is one that practices thoughtful reflexivity. Reflexivity, as we define it, is the capacity of an organization to observe, assess, evaluate, reflect on, and reform its knowledge systems. We introduced reflexivity briefly in Chapter 1, and here we want to offer some practical ideas for thinking about how to focus and implement it. Reflexivity is job number one for knowledge professionals. The focus of reflexivity is on establishing a synoptic view of the key knowledge systems operating within an organization and its surrounding contexts and asking fundamental questions about whether those systems are adequate to the tasks being put to them. If they are, great. If not, then change is needed. Many organizations have become much more reflexive in recent years regarding the importance of data and data systems, but data systems are only one element of knowledge systems. Knowledge systems also include a variety of additional elements that must also be attended to, as we described in earlier chapters.

In the rest of this chapter, we highlight three key strategies for creating reflexive, knowledge-aware organizations. The first is improving the alignment of knowledge and decision making. The second is developing a framework and strategies for knowledge systems innovation: the regular monitoring, evaluation, and upgrading of knowledge systems. The third is building a professional capacity for knowledge systems management within the organization.

Improving the Alignment of Knowledge and Action

A key facet of reflexive knowledge systems practice for an organization is ensuring appropriate alignment between how knowledge gets made and used. We have discussed aspects of this challenge throughout the book, but it is worth summarizing that discussion here and extending and expanding it to some degree.

The most common model for aligning knowledge and action is instrumental.[1] By instrumental, we mean that there is a goal to achieve or a decision to make and knowing something can improve our ability to achieve the goal or make a good decision. In instrumental terms, knowledge generally serves as a source of information. In one of the examples at the beginning of this chapter, for example, an organization confronted problems in its supply chain. By creating a knowledge system that identified those problems early, managers could step in and fix problems before they could become serious. This is an example of a knowledge system serving an instrumental purpose. Similarly, the nutritional information placed on food packages, such as breakfast cereals, that we discussed in Chapters 2 and 3 is also primarily intended as an instrumental knowledge system. People can make better eating decisions if they know the nutritional content of their food. Other instrumental knowledge for that decision might include their family's preferences in breakfast cereals and which stores sell preferred brands at the lowest prices.

Aligning knowledge and action instrumentally is simple to say: make sure that you have the right knowledge to make a good decision or take the right action. Unfortunately, as we've suggested throughout this book, it's harder to put into practice. Good knowledge may not be available without significant investments of time or money. Even with good knowledge, there may be residual uncertainties that complicate or foil good decision making. Or, there may be too much information, in too many competing forms. All of this can contribute to a failure to align knowledge and action: somehow, we don't get the knowledge we need to make a good decision.

Presently, eating well is a good case of too much information. The amount of competing diet and nutritional information in the marketplace is enormous. Having nutritional information on food packages is helpful, but figuring out how to translate that into a proper diet is complicated by the variety of diet advice available on the internet, in books, and from your doctor, your friends and neighbors, and your parents (or kids).

In such circumstances, most of us take the approach of focusing in on one or at most a few key sources of advice, whether it's our own sensibilities, our doctor, or a particular diet. And then we focus in on the particular knowledge needs of that approach. For example, many current diets are low-carbohydrate or low-sugar. This creates a target. Nutritional labels can be used to count up the sugar content of the foods eaten each day and try to keep that number below a certain level. Another similar approach is a low glycemic index diet. The glycemic index measures the body's blood sugar and insulin response to sugar. The goal is to eat foods that do not raise blood sugar and insulin levels. This is more complex than just measuring sugars, and the glycemic index isn't reported on food packages. Hence, the user must rely instead on books that estimate (based on research) the glycemic index of different foods, using the information contained in the books to construct a daily diet.

This kind of alignment of knowledge and action—developing a decision framework and then focusing in on the knowledge necessary to implement that framework—is so common that scholars have given it a name: co-production.[2] Co-production literally means to produce knowledge and organization or knowledge and action together. The idea of co-production originally emerged in the theoretical social sciences but has increasingly received attention among those trying to improve the utility of knowledge for decision-makers.[3]

In the case of the glycemic index diet, co-production refers, in part, to an individual's choice to adopt a decision framework (eating low glycemic index foods) and the knowledge system necessary to support it (a table of the glycemic index of different food items). But it also refers to the larger enterprise that supports that effort. Groups of doctors have published books that recruit people to choose that decision framework and contain the appropriate table of information (as well as the evidence designed to persuade people to choose a glycemic index diet).[4] Based on the idea that glycemic index information is important, especially for people with diabetes, governments have funded researchers to calculate the glycemic index for most major food items, so that it is possible to create the relevant tables. The result is a network of researchers, doctors, and individuals and families all organized around knowing and eating in a certain way.

Co-production is great when it works. In this case, if the low glycemic index diet works as a knowledge system tied to specific actions, many people either lose weight or keep their diabetes under control — and thus improve overall health outcomes. But co-production can also go wrong. We're no longer talking about failing to align knowledge and action (as we did a few paragraphs back). Instead, when co-production goes wrong, it's because knowledge and action get aligned improperly. There are two major failure modes for co-production. One is to inappropriately skew knowledge to action: to look for evidence that supports choices already made, rather than considering the full range of evidence available. This kind of confirmation bias is well known, for individuals and organizations, as people filter the information that comes to them based on their preexisting beliefs. The second is to skew decision making to knowledge: to organize decision-making frameworks and processes around the knowledge available, simply because it is the knowledge available. For example, even though people are increasingly aware that future weather patterns are likely to be quite different than in the past, a great deal of infrastructure is still being designed and built based on historic weather data. In both cases, the result is the same: organizational lock-in that prevents a full examination of evidence and consideration of the potential action strategies available.

So how can organizations avoid inappropriate lock-in? One approach is joint knowledge creation among diverse knowledge producers and diverse users or stakeholders.[5] This approach helps ensure that co-production doesn't fall into simple traps, such as knowledge producers assuming they know what users need to know; knowledge consumers not appropriately interpreting uncertainty regarding knowledge claims; and no single approach to knowing or acting being dominant simply because of the exclusion of others. Jointly working together can increase the ability of knowledge producers to understand what knowledge users need, as well as how and when they need that knowledge. It can also help knowledge users understand the strengths and limitations of data and create credible pathways of communication between the two groups that facilitate not only effective knowledge transfer but also opportunities to grow or alter knowledge systems as conditions change or users expand their problem sets. And it can ensure that critical evaluations of any knowledge claims or decision frameworks are heard and evaluated. Of course, balancing the power dynamics of such an exercise can be extremely difficult, especially where knowledge hierarchies (perceptions of the relative value of different kinds of evidence, e.g., science vs. non-science or physical vs. social sciences) or decision hierarchies (e.g., corporate chains of command) exist.

When knowledge producers and users work effectively together to advance knowledge creation (and, potentially, validation, communication, and application), it can significant enhance the usability of knowledge. Scholars David Cash, Bill Clark, and their colleagues have written extensively about usable science or usable knowledge.[6] In their approach, usability means, first and foremost, salience and timeliness. Knowledge must be relevant and informative to solutions to the problem at hand and delivered in appropriate ways, at appropriate times, and to appropriate people so as to allow users to effectively act on it. In this fashion, users will be able to achieve their desired goals and outcomes. Knowledge also needs to be credible, in the sense that decision-makers find it and its source(s) to be believable and reliable. In turn, that knowledge needs to be communicated well, in ways that are salient, credible, and legitimate. This requires close coordination between those who are defining problems, those who are creating knowledge, and those who are using the resulting knowledge to make and evaluate organizational decisions and guide organizational strategies. Thus, approaches to usable knowledge and joint knowledge creation tend to work well when the problem confronting an organization is one of producer-user coordination. If an organization's knowledge systems aren't connecting the dots between producers and users in this fashion, then it's time to get to work to figure out why not and upgrade them.

What makes joint knowledge creation successful—when it works—is that it creates direct and immediate feedback loops between knowledge producers and users, allowing for close collaboration and coordination.[7] These feedback loops are a primary driver of co-production. Especially in contexts where knowledge producers and users have been isolated from one another and allowed to evolve in different directions (e.g., between academic researchers and policymakers), reestablishing tighter feedback loops can dramatically help improve the usability of knowledge and its impact on decision making.

There are also many other, more indirect, mechanisms through which feedback loops can occur, however. These mechanisms all work to tighten the links between knowledge making and decision making. For example, looping can occur through organizational investments in knowledge making and knowledge-making capabilities. When businesses invest heavily in one area of knowledge (e.g., financial accounting for shareholders), they can then become beholden to that knowledge simply because they now have much more extensive and specific knowledge in that domain than in others. Shifting gears to make decisions on other criteria may subsequently require making comparable investments in other knowledge domains, an expensive proposition. That is precisely what organizations have found over the past couple of decades in the field of sustainability, for example. To effectively integrate sustainability in decision making requires significantly upgrading the organization's knowledge system to produce a wide range of additional, often novel information.[8] Looking forward, many organizations are now realizing that they need to make yet another set of knowledge investments around climate risks, vulnerability, adaptation, and resilience and still another one around the social and ethical responsibilities inherent in technology innovation.[9] Pressures to make these investments are coming from diverse directions, including shareholders, customers, regulators, employees, and leaders.

Another avenue for looping occurs via knowledge application. In this case, the use of a type of knowledge reinforces the conditions for creating knowledge of that type and decreases the utility of other types of knowledge. For example, when censuses categorize people into categories (e.g., by race or class), organizations then tend to then make decisions (e.g., about diversity in hiring or targeted market-ing) using that information (since it's readily available and credible). Indeed, they are often asked or compelled to do so by other organizations, such as the courts. To accomplish this, organizations, in turn, often need to pursue additional knowledge about the people in those same categories, fur-ther deepening the commitment to those categories both in the ways people pursue research and the ways that they define problems and see and act in the world.[10] Looping can also occur in credibility performances. If someone pre-sents knowledge claims that we ultimately come to mis-trust, that can loop back around and negatively impact our judgment of his or her credibility — and vice versa.[11]

The importance of feedback loops in co-production is both what enables stability in knowledge systems and what creates the potential for transformative change. As we de-scribed in Chapter 4, knowledge systems are rarely static. Rather, both knowledge systems and the organizations they are integral to are dynamic and evolve over time. When a knowledge system appears to work reasonably well for an organization, the organization will typically in-vest new resources into making it more sophisticated and better able to inform key decisions. At the same time, the organization will typically invest more of its resources in decisions that draw on information from that knowledge system. This creates dynamic feedback loops in which the organization's decision processes become increasingly de-pendent on and intertwined with the relevant knowledge systems, thus creating stability around what an organiza-tion knows and how it acts. This stability can be highly val-uable for an organization, as it allows for optimization of performance around key goals and standards.

Similarly, co-production can drive transformative change. Because co-production occurs through dynamic in-teractions among diverse elements of knowledge systems and the organizations and networks they're embedded in, changes that begin to get a toehold can, over time, spread throughout organizations and networks and result in broad changes to the forms, routines, practices, and outcomes of decisions and actions.[12] Climate change is a great example. When scientists first highlighted that the Earth's climate system was changing, in the late 1950s, little notice was taken. Over time, however, the number of scientists conducting research on the phenomenon grew, across a growing number of disciplines. Activist organizations began to focus on the issue, emphasizing the need for political action. International negotiations followed, leading to the 1992 UN Framework Convention on Climate Change and a host of subsequent agreements over the next twenty-five years. Today, other actors are piling on. Cities and businesses, especially, have begun to declare in large numbers their intentions to go 100% carbon-neutral over the next few decades. Throughout this effort, the knowledge base supporting both efforts to understand climate change, evaluate its risks, and develop viable strategies for combatting it have grown apace.[13] In the most recent episode, as we finalize this manuscript, shareholders have just voted against management at Exxon to force the company to develop and report publicly on the economic risks it faces as a company due to growing climate policies by governments. It seems likely that this new knowledge system, created through political action within the company's governance structure, will likely reverberate through broad financial networks as well as the company's own management.

Before we leave this section, we should make two other important points about the appropriate alignment of knowledge and action. First, alignment can occur around diverse models of governance, that is, models of the proper relationship between knowledge and action, not just the instrumental or informational model we've been discussing.

Second, alignment and feedback loops can occur on multiple scales, not just the organizational scale that we've been discussing.

The model of knowledge as information is only one of many ways that knowledge and knowledge systems connect to organizational actions or decisions. For example, knowledge may be symbolic, rather than instrumental. One reason to put nutritional knowledge on food packages is to provide information to consumers. Another is to signal to those same consumers that they should be paying attention to the nutritional content of the food they're eating. Nutritional information thus also performs a symbolic purpose.

The climate change knowledge system example that we have discussed at many points in the book also has a critical symbolic purpose. Countries compile greenhouse gas emissions inventories in part so that they know how to reduce their disruption of the climate system but also in part to symbolically demonstrate to their neighbors that they are doing their part for the planet. Scientists have likewise compiled evidence of the reality and risks of climate change in part to inform decision making but also as part of a political fight over whether to take the actions necessary to reduce greenhouse gas emissions. This latter purpose is also symbolic and involves a model of governance that we might describe as a model of political conflict. In this model, governance is primarily understood in terms of the occurrence, negotiation, and resolution (or lack thereof) of political disputes between competing interest groups. In the United States, especially with respect to the environment, science is often used to help symbolically adjudicate or resolve political conflict. Thus, some knowledge systems involved in environmental policy (although certainly not all) are organized symbolically rather than instrumentally.

There are a wide variety of models of governance that operate within and across organizations. Here's a brief, illustrative list of some of the most common, along with a brief description of the role of knowledge systems within them:

- **Instrumental**: Governance through informed choices. By producing knowledge, knowledge systems provide evidence and information to be factored into decision making.

- **Political**: Governance through competition among parties or factions. By creating and communicating knowledge with high social meaning and visibility, the system helps establish significant political symbols that play to the strengths of different parties.

- **Problem-solving**: Governance through the identification and solving of problems. By identifying and analyzing problems, the system helps to establish and frame common reference points for governance institutions. By analyzing potential solutions and assessing solutions after implementation, the system also may operate in more instrumental mode.

- **Deliberation**: Governance by reasoned debate and argumentation. By raising the profile of key ideas or issues, the system encourages robust public and/or policy deliberation of them. Knowledge systems also contribute significantly to informing the positions of individuals or groups within these debates.

- **Allocation of power**: Governance through the exercise of power. By determining which ideas will matter—and whose ideas will matter—in making choices, the system exercises power as part of governance regimes.

- **Community-building**: Governance through the mobilization of community ties. By engaging diverse experts and/or other stakeholders and helping them learn about one another, the system builds communities with shared ideas and values and can position those communities to act on those ideas and values.

- **Trust-building**: Governance through the creation of trusted relationships between leaders and publics. By engaging publics in credible ways, especially regarding public trust that decision-makers see problems as they do and understand their knowledge, concerns, and perspectives, the system helps to shore up public confidence in the management of complex social and/or technical problems.

For each model of governance, knowledge systems play a significant but distinct role. An organization that is attentive to the specific goals being sought out for governance can develop knowledge systems that are more properly aligned with those goals. For instance, if the goal is to allocate power, for example, as it is in democratic elections, then there is a need for strong knowledge systems that are authoritative across all participants. When elections don't generate clear winners, e.g., because people dispute the accuracy of ballot totals, it undermines democracy and the ability of elections to facilitate a peaceful and orderly transition of power between competing parties. By contrast, if the goal is to promote robust, reasoned debates that ensure the appropriate voicing and consideration of a diversity of perspectives, then creating strong, singular, authoritative knowledge systems is likely to be the wrong approach. Such a system will tend to suppress dissenting views, not bring them out in the open to be heard and engaged. Instead, a better approach would be to foster multiple knowledge systems that support divergent ways of framing problems and different methods for generating, validating, and communicating knowledge claims.

A second important observation is that co-production operates at multiple scales. Most of what we have described thus far emphasizes the scale of an organization, but organizations are embedded in co-production processes that are both smaller and larger. Here we describe a simple taxonomy on three levels that organizations should be aware of: paradigm, organization, and network.

- **Paradigm** is the level of knowledge conceptualization and practice. As we've argued throughout this book, knowledge comes in packages that frame, order, and arrange it, according to particular epistemological and ontological assumptions about how to make knowledge and what kinds of things it is possible to know things about.[14] Co-production occurs at the paradigm level by orchestrating how we package knowledge with values and assumptions about order. Knowledge, data, hypotheses, and theories are value-laden. They depend on tacit assumptions, judgments, and framings of a variety of kinds that cannot be easily disentangled from the underlying factual information. The assumptions and problem-framings that shape data collection, and the standards and disciplinary conventions used to interpret and evaluate data, all shape and structure the knowledge that is ultimately generated and shared. For example, if we label a certain kind of group of individuals as a family and collect data about them, we are not merely engaged in a knowledge exercise. We are also embedding the social idea of a family into that knowledge from the outset. Geoffrey Bowker and Susan Leigh Starr excellently describe this level of co-production in their book *Sorting Things Out*.[15] They show that when we embed assumptions about value-laden concepts such as family-ness into data systems, that choice has real consequences when the resulting knowledge is both created and applied, such that it loops back into the ways organizations view and engage real families and, thus, affects real families.

- **Organization** is the level of the organization itself. On this level, co-production means aligning the organization, practices, and content of knowledge production within the organization with the institutional needs and arrangements of organizational decision making or governance.[16] This has two key components. As we highlighted, in Chapters 2 and 3, knowledge doesn't just happen; rather, it must be made. Knowledge is, in other words, the product of social and institutional organization and practices. At the same time, organizations rely heavily on their knowledge systems. The knowledge that organizations have available—and just as importantly, the things that they do not know—shape the ways that organizations understand the problems they confront, the opportunities that they have available, the solutions that may help them, the workings of their competitors, etc.

- **Network** is the level at which multiple organizations interact with each other and with their environment. As we discussed in Chapter 4, and in the example of climate transformation earlier in this section, knowledge is not just limited in use to inside organizations. Knowledge is often a crucial element in multi-organizational negotiations and collaborations. In these settings, organizations need to engage and work closely with others outside the organization, whether with customers, stakeholders, shareholders, partners, regulators, or broader publics.[17] Co-production reminds us that others may look at, know, and act in the world differently, reflecting divergent ways of framing problems and collecting and interpreting data, different standards or frameworks of validation, and alternative pathways for communicating and applying knowledge. The more thoroughly an organization understands why knowledge conflicts arise, the more capably it can act in the face of those differences. More importantly, co-production highlights the significance of finding strategies, as Sheila Jasanoff has eloquently put it, to reason together with others who reason differently from us.[18]

Co-production is a powerful tool for building a reflexive understanding of knowledge systems. Its basic message is that knowledge and action will tend to align over time—and that can explain a lot about how knowledge systems behave. Figuring out whether that alignment is appropriate or not—including figuring out whether the alignment is happening at the right scale and around the right model of governance—and acting to correct it when it's not, is what makes knowledge system management challenging. It's also the subject of the next section, on knowledge systems innovation.

Innovating Knowledge Systems

Organizations can pursue a variety of strategies to upgrade and innovate their knowledge systems, drawing on the ideas of co-production and reflexivity just described. In this section, we divide the process of assessing and upgrading knowledge systems into three phases:

1. **Monitoring and evaluating**: An organization should have a good understanding of its knowledge systems, how they are designed to work, and their strengths and limitations; it should know which ones are linked to core organizational values and decisions and which ones are more peripheral; it should monitor how they work in practice and their routine performance; and it should analyze and assess the consequences of specific knowledge design choices.

2. **Stress testing**: An organization should develop strategies for testing knowledge systems to identify conditions and circumstances under which failures might occur, develop strategies for responding to failures, and explore options for strengthening knowledge systems. In doing this, an organization will need to analyze and assess the relationships among assumptions, models, and variables incorporated into knowledge systems and their implications for outcomes that matter.

3. **Upgrading and innovating**: Finally, an organization should be particularly attentive to changing circumstances that might alter the probabilities that its knowledge systems might fail and should, when appropriate, upgrade knowledge systems or innovate new ones to address changed circumstances.

Following these steps can help ensure that an organization acts in a reflexive, knowledge-aware fashion.

1. Monitoring and Evaluating

If an organization doesn't already have one, it should seriously consider developing an independent evaluative capacity, whether internal or external, to identify, understand, monitor, and assess the knowledge systems they operate. Put simply, organizations need to know how their knowledge systems are designed to work, whether they work that way in practice, the range within which they can be reliably counted upon, the conditions under which they are likely to fail, and how to respond when they do.

In principle, the need for such a capacity is well known. In the case of financial risk assessment, for example, this role is performed by ratings agencies, which provide an independent evaluation of the riskiness of an asset. It's also why the Securities and Exchange Commission is supposed to monitor both companies and the ratings agencies. And it is why companies have independent auditors to look at their books. Yet, time and time again, we see these systems fail in ways that should have been anticipated. In all three of the cases of knowledge failure that we explored in Chapter 1, for example, there is clear evidence that knowledge systems had been neglected, atrophied, or deliberately distorted or degraded for various purposes — and that the results had contributed significantly to the knowledge failures. Too much is at stake for organizations, and for society, to continue to view these knowledge systems as anything less than critical infrastructure and to give them the attention they thus deserve.

Hurricane Katrina offers a good illustration of a case study in which greater effort to monitor and evaluate knowledge systems could potentially have paid off. It's not hard to understand why this wasn't done, of course. For many people, the challenge for New Orleans from the 1960s onward was to get a hurricane protection system built. Once that system was built, an integrated suite of levees and pumps would protect the city from flooding. Where was the need for effective knowledge systems, once the original design was complete? There is, unfortunately, an all-too-common assumption that infrastructure or other technologies are primarily physical entities. Yet, as the U.S. federal government and many companies are increasingly highlighting, most physical infrastructures are now being tightly interwoven with data systems to create cyber-physical systems. And, of course, the reality is that infrastructure systems have always been tightly connected to knowledge systems that informed not only their design but also their management, operation, upkeep, and redesign over time. Such knowledge systems are often hidden, and one part of a robust knowledge systems initiative is to find and reveal those knowledge systems to prevent exactly the kinds of failures that occurred in New Orleans.

In the case of the New Orleans hurricane protection system, for example, external reviews of the knowledge systems conducted after Hurricane Katrina revealed some important insights that could have been very useful to the city.[19] Perhaps the most significant addressed the standard to which the hurricane protection system had been designed. Engineers had followed a widely accepted practice of designing to a storm with a one percent chance of occurring in any given year. Such a storm is often referred to as a 1-in-100-year event or simply a 100-year storm. But what kind of storm is that? Knowing the answer requires delving into the knowledge system. The external review revealed that the design storm or 100-year storm, in this case officially called the Standard Project Hurricane, had been modeled by the U.S. Army Corps of Engineers based on data available to them in 1957. Historically, this makes sense, given the timing of the design of the hurricane protection system in the 1960s. By the 2000s, however, another 50 years of data was available on the frequency and intensity of hurricanes along the Gulf Coast. Had anyone looked at the Standard Project Hurricane model in the years running up to Hurricane Katrina, they would have found that the model significantly underestimated the strength of a 1-in-100-year hurricane. Had city leaders known that, they would have understood that their city was at greater risk than the design specs suggested they were.

So how can organizations do better? The first thing to do, and we discuss this in greater detail below given its overall significance, is to establish a cadre of knowledge system professionals who are responsible for overseeing the organization's knowledge systems. The idea of co-production reminds us that knowledge systems work is organizational work, and so it behooves organizations to organize, systematize, and prioritize that work as a key aspect of what the organization does and how it works. Given the growing centrality of data collection and analysis to many organizational knowledge systems, this could be organized as a function of the organization's information officer. However, there are two key things to watch out for when going this route. The first is that knowledge is not data, and many organizational knowledge systems do not involve digital information. The second is that many information officers are focused on technology, and while information technology (IT) systems do matter for a portion of knowledge systems, the real heart of knowledge systems is found in the knowledge and ideas that flow through data, email, and other IT systems — and through alternative social and technical arrangements — and arguably less the information technologies themselves. In creating a cadre of knowledge professionals, it is important to recognize that the goals are to empower a group of people to take responsibility for ensuring that knowledge systems function well; but also to build a capacity for reflexivity in knowledge systems that is distributed throughout the organization.

The second step is for an organization to catalog its diverse knowledge systems and to classify them for priority of review. This is not a simple task, especially in large or complex organizations, so it may be preferable to start with those systems that are well known and central to the organization's activities. Yet, as we suggested above, hidden knowledge systems can carry significant weight. In the end, two categories are particularly important: those knowledge systems for which a major failure would create serious risk for the organization and those where opportunities exist to significantly upgrade the performance of the organization through knowledge system innovation.

The third step is to create a set of routines, practices, and directives for monitoring and evaluating the production and use of knowledge within the organization on an ongoing basis. These routines and practices are the basis for becoming a reflexive knowledge organization. This effort can take many forms. It may start, for example, with some sort of top-down review. In the end, however, most organizations are going to find that their knowledge systems are too extensive and too complex to review regularly from the top or the outside. Instead, a critical objective for any organization—and its knowledge systems professionals—is to infuse reflexivity throughout the culture of the organization's knowledge systems. Those participating in knowledge systems should understand that they are doing so, what their role is, and why it matters, as well as take (and be granted) the initiative to assess how the knowledge system is functioning, what assumptions it is working with, whether those assumptions remain appropriate, and how the knowledge system can be improved. In the end, then, the goal must be to establish a culture of knowledge systems reflexivity.

2. Stress Testing

Reflexivity requires knowing not only how knowledge systems tick but also testing their reliability under a variety of potential scenarios for future failure. For this very reason, the concept of stress testing has become common in critical industries that are "too big to fail." The same idea can be applied to knowledge systems that are "too important to fail."

The concept of stress testing is built on the principle that it is possible to identify an array of potential future scenarios that would test the limits of an existing knowledge system's functioning. The goal is to assess the sensitivity of a knowledge system to diverse future conditions and pathways and to see under what conditions and pathways it will continue to produce reliable knowledge and under what conditions and pathways it will begin to produce problematic claims. In mathematical modeling, for example, formal efforts are sometimes undertaken to determine the boundaries of reliability or validity for any given model. So long as the model is operating within those boundaries, then its results are valid. Outside those boundaries, it is no longer valid. The same idea lies behind tests of statistical validity, which give a confidence interval within which one can have reasonable confidence that one has found a real correlation and not just a statistical aberration.

Stress testing is the expansion of ideas of measuring the boundaries of reliability from a model or statistical analysis to the whole knowledge system. For example, to continue the discussion of Hurricane Katrina from the previous section, when the U.S. Army Corps of Engineers constructed the Standard Project Hurricane for the New Orleans levees, they could have not just built the model but also stress tested it to see under what conditions it would have begun to break down. One such set of conditions that would have emerged would have been the case that the frequency and intensity of hurricanes along the Gulf Coast would have increased over time. At that point, climate change was relatively unknown, so they likely couldn't have anticipated that such a change was going to occur. Their stress testing would have told the city's knowledge professionals to pay careful attention to monitoring the data on hurricane frequency and intensity, however. And, then, if those factors did increase, as they did, the community could have considered how to respond to those changes.

Stress testing could also have significantly helped organizations trying to protect Flint, Michigan, from risks to their health from water contamination. We described the relevant knowledge systems briefly in Chapter 1 and explored, specifically, the way that testing for the presence of lead in the water supply is carried out. In relation to this testing regime, which was woefully inadequate, the city or the state could have conducted a stress test. Instead of just following the existing testing practices as required by law, they could have made efforts to determine the likelihood of errors occurring as well as the circumstances under which errors would be most likely. Likewise, they could have evaluated the consequences of a knowledge failure and asked whether that level of risk was acceptable. Finally, they could have occasionally done more rigorous sampling, to see how the results of routine tests stood up to a more ambitious look at the problem.

This kind of analysis is frequently done in medical diagnostics. When new tests are developed, they are often subjected to a rigorous analysis that asks a series of questions: (1) how frequently and under what conditions does the test correctly identify a disease when it is present (and, therefore, also, when does it fail to identify that disease even though it is present); (2) how frequently and under what conditions does the test incorrectly say that a disease is present when it is not (and, therefore, also, when does it correctly say that no disease is present); and (3) what are the impacts of incorrect diagnoses.

This is a variant of a stress test that would have been handy for Flint officials to carry out—and which is generally valuable for many knowledge systems. Maybe the city or state did these things, but, if so, they behaved strangely when evidence began to appear that raised questions about the veracity of their knowledge claims. That's a key time for knowledge systems and one when stress tests can be particularly important. It's unclear what would have happened in Flint had the official knowledge system described thus far continued as the sole source of insight into the problem of lead in Flint's water supply.

Fortunately for Flint residents, it didn't. Three groups begin to innovate their knowledge systems and challenge the official narrative. First, residents themselves began diagnosing significant problems with the water. Beginning in the summer of 2014, city residents began to complain of visual contamination, strange odors and tastes, and, especially troubling, an array of new health concerns. These problems were reported to the Mayor's office, at City Council meetings, to the Flint water utility, and through other mechanisms. Some city residents even had their own water tests done, some of which showed highly elevated levels of lead. Sadly, as is often the case with bureaucratic knowledge systems, which often suffer from the kinds of knowledge systems lock-in described earlier in this chapter, these reports were discounted in the face of a belief in the data provided by the federally mandated water sampling routines that showed that lead levels were below legally problematic limits. In part, this act of neglect reflects a legal culture of self-protection. The law requires that people follow the mandated procedures, so they do. In part, it also reflects a culture of belief in the system: surely if this is what the Environmental Protection Agency (EPA) requires, then the resulting data would show a problem if there was one. But it can also reflect a form of inertia: Hey, this is how we do things here.

When one city resident received a private water test indicating high lead levels in her water, she contacted regional EPA officials. One of those officials ultimately put her in touch with a lab at Virginia Tech University that specialized in lead testing. When that lab tested her water, they found extremely high levels and became very concerned. They subsequently formed an advocacy group, the Flint Water Study, which sent 300 water sampling kits to people across the city, asking them to collect samples using the lab's preferred methods for sample collection. They discovered when they analyzed the samples much higher levels of lead contamination across the entire city than the Flint water utility had found. Where the city had found two wards within the city to have elevated lead levels in more than 10% of the samples, the Flint Water Study found more than 10% of samples had elevated lead levels in all 9 city wards. By their measure, the 90th percentile metric for Flint was 25 parts per billion (ppb), almost double the legal limit. This information was released on September 8, 2015.

A third knowledge system then came into play. Pondering news of the Flint Water Study, a team of pediatricians at one of Flint's hospitals realized that they had access to data that would tell them whether children in the city had higher levels of lead in their blood. What they found confirmed the Flint Water Study's fears: lead in the city's water supply was also in the city's children. On September 24, 2015, the team, led by Dr. Mona Hanna-Attisha, held a press conference to announce their results. On October 16, 2015, the city changed its water supply. On January 22, 2016, the Obama Administration declared a state of emergency in Flint, and the EPA took over responsibility for the safety of Flint's water supply from the Michigan Department of Environmental Quality (MDEQ).

The case of Flint's water supply demonstrates why it is so crucial for organizations to stress test their knowledge systems. It also demonstrates another important potential strategy of stress testing: the idea of comparing results using alternative knowledge systems.

While public attention has quickly shifted away from questions of knowledge to questions of politics and accountability, taking responsibility for the proper functioning of knowledge systems is the only real way to address the long-term problem of knowledge failures. In this case, three government organizations (the city, MDEQ, and EPA) went through their required procedures but did little else to ascertain what was going on, even in the face of significant expressions of public concern. By contrast, three other organizations (city residents, the Flint Water Study, and a team of pediatricians) took significant actions to take ownership of the problem and implement knowledge systems that revealed a very different picture of what was going on.

For any organization, knowledge failures take a wide variety of forms, from failing to know what is going on inside the organization to failing to know what is going on outside the organization to failing to generate, validate, circulate, and apply the new ideas, insights, and innovations necessary for long-term organizational success. The only way to avoid these failures is to know what the organization knows, how and why it knows those things (and not others), what the limits of the organization's knowledge systems are (what it doesn't know), and how knowledge systems can be improved over time in response to new challenges. Creating, communicating, and putting this meta-knowledge to use is the job of knowledge professionals.

3. Upgrading and Innovating

In both cases described thus far, change has been an important contributor to knowledge failure. It should be obvious by now, but knowledge systems are generally designed to meet the needs of organizations confronting particular circumstances. Unfortunately, circumstances change, and when they do, knowledge systems need to change, too. Unfortunately, that doesn't always happen.

How should an organization approach the upgrading of knowledge systems? There is rarely only one right way, but our general recommendation is to draw heavily on the frameworks and tools presented in earlier chapters, as well as the ideas of co-production described above. Using the framework described in Chapter 2, for example, an organization can initiate any knowledge system upgrade with a mapping exercise that identifies all relevant components and parts of the system and how they relate to one another. Using the framework elaborated in Chapter 3, the organization can focus in on the various functions of the knowledge system, see how each function maps onto the component parts, identify where breakdowns are occurring, and repair or improve them. Finally, drawing on Chapter 4, the organization can assess where system dynamics either are now or could in the future contribute to knowledge failures. In all of this, the organization can focus on understanding where and how knowledge systems are feeding into crucial decisions and where and how, in turn, social and organizational practices are shaping knowledge outcomes.

We have been working recently on a problem that illustrates what a knowledge system upgrade might look like, while also revealing some of the complexities that can come into play. The focus of the overall project is to improve the resilience of cities to future climate risks. Our part of the project is specifically focused on urban knowledge systems and how they can be upgraded. We are working with several cities and have begun to analyze the ways in which those cities produce and use knowledge of different kinds in designing and planning urban infrastructures and their resilience to diverse kinds of risks.

In mapping urban knowledge systems, following the approach laid out in Chapters 2 and 3, we found one particular knowledge artifact with very high significance called a design storm. As we described briefly for the case of the New Orleans hurricane protection system, a design storm is a standard used in the design of infrastructure to specify the size or type of storm that the infrastructure is meant to be able to protect against. Every city in the world is built on (and its citizens depend on for protection from risks and delivery of services) a constellation of infrastructures: roads, bridges, sewers, storm water drainage, dikes and levees, water delivery, electricity grids, fuel pipelines, communication systems, and more. Each of those infrastructures has been designed by engineers to meet certain design standards. Among the most important inputs into project design are models of the weather that the infrastructure will experience over the course of its useful life: the rainfall that it will be exposed to, the temperature extremes that it will experience, and the winds that will buffet it.

Those models are often called design storms or design floods.

A design storm is a fact-value hybrid, as we defined the term in Chapter 2. It embeds values regarding how much risk a community feels safe taking on. A common approach is for a community to say that they want to protect against a 100-year storm or flood, meaning that they want the frequency of infrastructure failure to be less than once every 100 years, or a one percent chance of it occurring on any given year. To this risk standard, the design storm then adds empirical knowledge about the frequency with which storms of particular intensity and duration occur, enabling the calculation of the intensity and duration of storm that the infrastructure needs to design for. This is commonly expressed in terms of a maximum temperature exposure or rainfall level over a specified time. The Standard Project Hurricane used in the design of the New Orleans levee system, for example, expressed its measures in terms of maximum wind speed, rainfall, and storm surge during a given hurricane event.

Unfortunately, changes are occurring that render existing design storm calculations problematic. Changes in extreme weather patterns are now altering the frequency and intensity of temperature, rainfall, and wind events. Statisticians call their data stationary if its statistical properties stay the same over time. For example, the weather would be stationary if the statistical frequency, intensity, and duration of rainfall were the same in the 1800s and 1900s as it is in the 2000s. This would allow scientists to measure these statistics historically and then use the data to inform decisions about future infrastructure design. By contrast, if the statistical properties of the weather change over time, statisticians term that behavior non-stationary. In that case, weather patterns from the 1800s and 1900s may no longer be as useful in telling planners how to prepare for tomorrow's extreme events.

The current methods of constructing design storms generally assume that the weather is statistically stationary, in that the method uses historical data to determine the weather for which future infrastructures must plan. By now, however, a wealth of observational evidence and model projections suggests that future weather patterns are unlikely to be the same in the future as they have in the past. This means that city planners and infrastructure engineers need to upgrade their design storm knowledge systems to account for this change from stationary weather patterns to non-stationary weather patterns.

What might such an upgrade look like? Here are four possible strategies that a city could take, each quite different in its approach. Each comes with important strengths and weaknesses, and each highlights the different ways that reflexivity and co-production can be used together to inform knowledge system upgrades.

- **Create a dynamic weather model**: The most obvious response to changing weather patterns is to attempt to model the changes to anticipate what future weather patterns may look like. Many approaches might work, from conducting trend analyses to working with predictive models. The advantages of this approach are that it doesn't significantly alter the process for deciding on infrastructure designs (just the relevant design criteria) and that it attempts to develop the best possible knowledge of future weather events for use in the design. The disadvantages include that model projections are always simply projections and may turn out to be incorrect, which adds uncertainty to the process (although all potential responses do that, in one way or another) and there are many possible models, so someone must decide which approach to take.

- **Design more robust infrastructure**: A second relatively obvious response is to design more robust infrastructure that can withstand a wider array of potential future conditions. This is a common approach to engineering safety design when the operating conditions are likely to change over the system's life. Bridges, for example, must be designed to handle high traffic flows, so engineers must anticipate how high those flows will be. Typically, however, since that projection is uncertain, designers will introduce a safety factor, e.g., by designing the bridge to handle twice the weight of the highest traffic projection. The upside is that this approach gives a much greater margin for avoiding failure. The downside is that it almost always adds cost.

- **Design safe-to-fail or adaptive infrastructure**: A third approach is to significantly alter the engineering design paradigm. Instead of designing to avoid infrastructure failures, cities are increasingly looking at strategies that involve infrastructure that is safe-to-fail, meaning that failures are expected and are designed to cause significantly less damage. Houses built on stilts are a simple example. They don't try to stop floods; they're designed to be safe even when it floods. Another approach is to design more easily adaptable infrastructure. Instead of designing infrastructure that must last for decades in the same form, design infrastructure that can be more easily and less expensively modified over time as future extreme weather patterns become clearer. The upsides of both approaches are that they likely significantly reduce the risks of building expensive infrastructure that either is unnecessary or fails spectacularly. The downsides are that they are likely to be somewhat more costly than current infrastructure designs and to raise difficult value questions, such as "safe-to-fail for whom?" In a recent example of using safe-to-fail approaches, for example, engineers managing water levels on the Mississippi River on multiple occasions spilled water into rural regions (farmlands and river deltas) to avoid flooding nearby cities. The results prevented extensive damage to the cities but certainly caused problems for farmers and other rural residents.

- **Readjust risk values**: A fourth potential approach to upgrading design storm knowledge systems is to re-adjust the risk values used to guide it. One can, for example, simply continue to use historical weather data to guide future infrastructure design, knowing that by doing so one is taking on additional risk of extreme events. The upside to this approach is that it is easy — all too easy in fact. In the face of uncertainty about future weather risks, virtually all cities world-wide have done little to nothing to alter their design storm calculations. Changing law and policy are often difficult, messy affairs, and design storms are generally legal standards that would have to be changed through the political process. The downsides include the fact that many city residents and leaders may be unaware that the city is exposing itself to new risks, unless the decision to leave the design standards the same is widely discussed. Also, the city may expose itself to legal liability, if future extreme events cause damage to residents based on what come to be seen as faulty design standards.

Design storms, or what we might call community climate knowledge systems, are generally a rather obscure act of law, based on expert knowledge that is rarely looked at too hard outside of the engineering community, as well as community value judgments made once upon a time and then embedded in the design of every facet of the community's infrastructure. Changing such knowledge systems is never an easy undertaking. So even if it might seem intuitive that the engineering design community and the city and community governments that invest heavily in infrastructure would be engaged in a process of upgrading their design storm definitions, most cities have not yet made the effort to update their knowledge systems. In this case, what's probably needed is a multi-stakeholder decision-making process that can explore and ultimately select from the array of potential strategies for expanding the range of variability encompassed by design storm standards. But, first, what's needed is an awareness that, even if they do nothing, cities are by default exposing themselves and their residents to new and additional risks. It's time for cities to acknowledge that fact and to engage in a deliberate initiative to review, stress test, and upgrade their knowledge systems.

Building a Team of Knowledge Systems Professionals

Reflexivity in knowledge systems — monitoring, testing, upgrading, and innovating — is never easy. Anyone who's ever participated in developing and refining a new reporting system knows that. Perhaps the most powerful illustration in recent years comes from the field of sustainability, as companies and public sector organizations have sought to figure out and implement new frameworks for evaluating the sustainability of their operations and supply chains. This has involved extensive knowledge work: to figure out how to define sustainability, to collect and analyze data, to figure out how to measure performance, and to reconfigure the organization to make sure that the resulting data is used effectively in business decisions. Alongside this knowledge work, businesses have also created a new cadre of sustainability professionals whose job is to reorient the company around new sustainability goals, practices, and information. These professionals receive different kinds of training than other employees. Similarly, the introduction of information systems and, more recently, big data has created new ranks of IT professionals and data analysts within businesses.

All three groups are knowledge professionals whose positions require them to attend carefully to making and using knowledge. But they rarely receive training specifically in knowledge systems analysis and innovation. Rather, they receive training in technical areas of knowledge making, e.g., sustainability indicators, information systems, and data systems. The technical work that goes on in these areas is extremely important, but it is only one facet of the larger knowledge systems that serve business decision making. Frequently, for example, technical training and specialization neglects the human dimensions of knowledge making, the strategies organizations can use to effectively review and communicate diverse knowledge claims, and the ways that organizations can evaluate, assess, and innovate knowledge systems to meet new challenges.

We argue, therefore, that organizations should invest in knowledge systems professionals: people trained specifically in creating, analyzing, and innovating knowledge systems and knowledge design. This does not necessarily mean adding a new corporate division or a new chief knowledge officer, although in some circumstances the latter might be warranted. At a minimum, it means ensuring that at least a few people in key places in the organization are well prepared to reflect on knowledge systems, how they behave and work, how they are organized, and how they generate, validate, communicate, and apply knowledge to key decisions. It likely also means familiarizing people from throughout the organization with key ideas and principles for effective knowledge systems operation.

Finally, we would also like to see significantly greater engagement between the business and policy communities and knowledge systems researchers. Knowledge systems have emerged as a major research topic within diverse fields, including information studies and science and technology studies, as well as disciplines like sociology and anthropology. Yet in many cases, this research tends to be highly theoretical and divorced from the meaningful work of real-world organizations. At the same time, most organizations continue to neglect knowledge systems analysis and design as an important focus of attention. Creating a new community of knowledge systems professionals, drawing from businesses, nonprofits, governments, and universities, could help create the basis for productive partnerships, use-inspired research, and, we hope, a long-term reduction in dangerous knowledge failures.

Chapter 5 Takeaways

- Strategies for creating a knowledge-aware organization include improving the alignment of knowledge and decision making; developing a framework and strategies for knowledge systems innovation; and building a professional capacity for knowledge systems management within the organization.

- Aligning knowledge and action is often a function of using knowledge instrumentally, so that the knowledge improves the ability to achieve a goal or make a good decision.

- Alignment can occur around diverse modes of governance (e.g., instrumental, political, problem-solving, deliberation, allocation of power, community-building, and trust building) and occur on multiple scales (e.g., paradigm, organization, and network).

- Organizations can pursue a variety of strategies to upgrade their knowledge systems, including monitoring and evaluating; stress-testing; and upgrading and innovating.

- Knowledge systems management requires building a team of knowledge systems professionals who are trained specifically in creating, analyzing, and innovating knowledge systems and knowledge design.

CONCLUSION: TAKING CONTROL OF KNOWLEDGE

We live in an era in which the veracity of truth claims is widely called into question. Some have even called it "post-truth," rejecting both the possibility of reliable knowledge and the idea that organizations and societies should rely on knowledge and expertise to inform good decisions.

In our view, this goes too far. Yes, uncertainty is widespread, as are deep-seated conflicts over both specific knowledge claims and broader concepts of how best to make knowledge. We argue in this book, however, that these challenges can be overcome. Knowledge can still be made useful. The way to make knowledge useful is to know where it came from, who made it, how it got together, and what its strengths and limitations are. Improved attention to knowledge systems can go a long way, even in today's polarized politics.

Organizations that understand how knowledge gets made, validated, communicated, and applied will better navigate the ins and outs of epistemic conflict. They will better understand the strengths and limitations of their knowledge systems, and those of others. They will have a better grasp on the reliability or uncertainty of the knowledge claims that they rely on to make critical decisions. They will be able to understand why different knowledge systems give rise to competing knowledge claims and thus be better able to help negotiate or settle conflicts. They will be better able to respond appropriately when faced with over-hyped claims based on unrealistic ideas of certainty, veracity, and truth. And they will be positioned to improve their knowledge through upgrades in knowledge systems design.

The reality is that the knowledge that organizations work with on a daily basis has never been absolute truth, and knowledge systems designs have always shaped knowledge claims. In the past, the significance of uncertainty, framing, and interpretive judgment were often ignored or downplayed, but the pretense of certainty didn't alter the way knowledge actually worked — or works today, in its myriad of guises. Knowledge has always been the product of organization, and the organization of knowledge making has always configured the resulting knowledge. Knowledge systems determine what knowledge is important and therefore what knowledge gets made, using what kinds of methods. They embed tacit and explicit assumptions. They work according to diverse epistemologies that set sometimes remarkably different standards for choosing and evaluating evidence and for handling uncertainty. They take very different approaches to reviewing, vetting, validating, and verifying knowledge claims and the people and processes used to generate it. And they adopt distinct frameworks for communicating, interpreting, assessing, evaluating, and applying knowledge.

Thus, not surprisingly, multiple knowledge systems frequently come into conflict with one another. Differences in knowledge systems lead people and organizations to see different aspects of a problem, interpret the significance of evidence according to different criteria, and come to different conclusions. As a result, people and organizations then understand and act in the world according to divergent rationalities, wrapping knowledge up in questions of power and politics.

Rigorous knowledge systems promise greater accuracy and reliability; they promise progress of a sort. But rigor cannot escape the inevitability of differences in design. Knowledge and the systems that create it are partial, limited, prone to errors and inaccuracies, and subject to differences in interpretation, emphasis, and valuation. A poet might call this the human condition. At some points in time and in some places, real or seeming agreement within society on how to make knowledge has reduced debates over the value and veracity of knowledge, but these debates are unavoidable. Disputes, and even conflicts, over knowledge and knowledge making are common in human history.

Organizations that want to thrive in competitive and polarized knowledge environments cannot simply assume that the ways they know things now (or the ways of knowing that are conducive to their interests) are the only right ways to know. We suggest that the goal, instead, should be to become knowledge-aware organizations, capable of understanding, analyzing, managing, and adapting their own knowledge systems and knowledge claims and the implications of those systems and claims for others outside their own organization. Increasing these capacities will significantly improve organizational performance and reduce the likelihood of significant knowledge errors or bad decision outcomes. They will also help avoid situations that have become increasingly prevalent in recent years, where knowledge and data systems have become significant sources of organizational bias and social and economic inequality.[1]

At the same time, knowledge-aware organizations should be aware of the complexity of knowledge dynamics in modern societies and be able to productively, proactively, and collaboratively manage their knowledge relationships with others, whether those are customers, stakeholders, partners, competitors, regulators, or critics. Rarely will this lend itself well to control, in which organizations can simply impose their notions of truth on others. Far more frequently, organizations will find themselves negotiating with others in order to find empathy with alternative problem framings, to temporarily reconcile differences, and to find mutually agreeable settlements.

Knowledge remains an enormous asset—the essential asset—even in an age of uncertainty, confusion, and dispute over the value of knowledge. The fact that truth and knowledge have limits cannot and should not mean that all claims are equal or that no consensus is possible about how to understand either the world or our place in it. The cure to persistent uncertainty is to pay careful attention to the practices of knowledge making.

ACKNOWLEDGEMENTS

We owe a great many thanks to the people and organizations who have helped us to develop and refine the ideas in this book.

Most importantly, we want to thank Eric Kennedy. Eric is one of the student leaders of the ASU School for the Future of Innovation in Society and one of the most important contributors to its research on knowledge, knowledge systems, and interdisciplinarity. He graciously reviewed the first draft of the manuscript and provided us with extensive feedback on our ideas and how best to present them. The book is much better as a result. We are also very grateful to Gregg Zachary and Jason Lloyd for their extensive help in editing and producing this book.

We first began to collaborate on the ideas in this book in a research seminar at Arizona State University over a decade ago. We are grateful to the many ASU students who explored those ideas with us in that seminar and many others since in the PhD programs in Sustainability and in Human and Social Dimensions of Science and Technology. Ann Kinzig and the Advancing Conservation in a Social Context project team supported our early work, gave us a concrete context for applying our ideas, and offered lots of constructive feedback. Chad Monfreda, who worked with us on that project, deserves special acknowledgment for his contributions to our first working paper on knowledge systems. Michelle Muñoz Dorna is always willing to contribute her graphic design skills with no expectation in return other than sisterly love. We are also excited to continue to be able to discuss our ideas with the current group of students, postdocs, and colleagues in the Knowledge Systems Innovation Task Force of the Urban Resilience to Extreme Weather-Related Events Sustainability Research Network (UREx SRN). Through the UREx SRN, we are putting our ideas to work with researchers and city managers to help cities adapt to climate change.

Our collaboration on knowledge systems has always been inspired and informed by the increasingly influential field of science and technology studies and its innovative insights into how people and organizations make knowledge. Most importantly, in writing this book and in many other ways, we have benefited from the insights of Sheila Jasanoff. More than any other, Sheila's comparative analyses of diverse settings where knowledge is made and used demonstrate that paying careful attention to the design of knowledge is essential to enabling institutions to make good decisions. We deeply appreciate her intellectual and professional leadership, inspiration, and guidance—and her friendship—over many years.

We are also thankful to the National Science Foundation, which has supported numerous projects that have helped develop the ideas in this book. Specific projects include the Decision Center for a Desert City (NSF 1462086), the Urban Resilience to Extreme Weather-Related Events Sustainability Research Network (NSF 1444755), the San Juan Urban Long-Term Research Area (NSF 0948507), and interdisciplinary, collaborative research and educational grants from several other programs on the topics of climate resilience, knowledge, and sustainability (NSF 1043289, 1140190, 1152872, 1360509, 1441352). Additional support provided by the U.S. Department of Agriculture Forest Service International Institute of Tropical Forestry and the University of Puerto Rico–Rio Piedras.

Finally, we are grateful for the support of our wonderful partners, Karin Ellison and Justin Erickson, who make every day amazing, and our awesome kids, Jay David Miller and Sofía Aimée Erickson, who light up our lives.

NOTES

CHAPTER 1: THE COST OF KNOWLEDGE FAILURES

[1] European Commission, Directorate-General for Research, *Taking European Knowledge Society Seriously*, Report of the Expert Group on Science and Governance to the Science, Economy and Society Directorate (Brussels, Belgium: European Commission, 2007). United Nations Educational, Scientific, and Cultural Organization, *Towards Knowledge Societies* (New York, NY: UNESCO, 2005). World Bank, *Building Knowledge Economies: Advanced Strategies for Development* (Washington, DC: World Bank, 2007).

[2] Three of the most important analyses of major knowledge failures are: C. Perrow, *Normal Accidents: Living with High-Risk Technologies* (Princeton, NJ: Princeton University Press, 1984); D. Vaughan, *The Challenger Launch Decision: Risky Technology, Culture, and Deviance at NASA* (Chicago, IL: University of Chicago Press, 1996); and D. MacKenzie, "The Credit Crisis as a Problem in the Sociology of Knowledge," *American Journal of Sociology* 116, no. 6 (2011): 1778-1841.

[3] N. Machiavelli, *The Prince* (Cambridge, UK: Cambridge University Press, 1988).

[4] World Bank, "Big Data in Action for Government" (2017). IBM, "Could Your Content be Working Harder — and Smarter?" (2014).

[5] C. Miller, T. A. Muñoz-Erickson, and C. Monfreda, "Knowledge Systems Analysis," Report #10-05, Consortium for Science, Policy & Outcomes (2010).

[6] S. Jasanoff, *Risk Management and Political Culture* (New York, NY: Russell Sage Foundation, 1986).

[7] See, for example: D. Bloor, *Knowledge and Social Imagery* (Chicago, IL: University of Chicago Press, 1976).

[8] D. W. Cash, "'In Order to Aid in Diffusing Useful and Practical Information': Agricultural Extension and Boundary Organizations," *Science, Technology, & Human Values* 26, no. 4 (2001): 431-453. D. W. Cash, et al., "Knowledge Systems for Sustainable Development," *Proceedings of the National Academy of Sciences* 100, no. 14 (2003): 8086-8091.

[9] B. Wynne, "Public Engagement as a Means of Restoring Public Trust in Science—Hitting the Notes, but Missing the Music?" *Public Health Genomics* 9, no. 3 (2006): 211-220. S. Jasanoff, "Civilization and Madness: The Great BSE Scare of 1996," *Public Understanding of Science* 6, no. 3 (1997): 221-232.

[10] D. MacKenzie, "The Credit Crisis as a Problem in the Sociology of Knowledge," *American Journal of Sociology* 116, no. 6 (2011): 1778-1841.

[11] B. Yandle, "Lost Truth: The Real Cause of the Financial Meltdown," Working Paper No. 09-02, Mercatus Center, George Washington University (2009).

[12] American Society for Civil Engineering, *The New Orleans Hurricane Protection System: What Went Wrong and Why: A Report* (Reston, VA: ASCE, 2007).

[13] American Society for Civil Engineering, *The New Orleans Hurricane Protection System: What Went Wrong and Why: A Report* (Reston, VA: ASCE, 2007), v.

[14] American Society for Civil Engineering, *The New Orleans Hurricane Protection System: What Went Wrong and Why: A Report* (Reston, VA: ASCE, 2007), vi-vii.

[15] Information for this section was obtained from public documents made available via the website of the Flint Water Study (http://flintwaterstudy.org), from the EPA, and from a report, "What Went Wrong in Flint?" published on the website fivethirtyeight.com (http://fivethirtyeight.com/features/what-went-wrong-in-flint-water-crisis-michigan/).

CHAPTER 2: HOW ORGANIZATIONS MAKE KNOWLEDGE

[1] C. W. Choo, *The Knowing Organization: How Organizations Use Information to Construct Meaning, Create Knowledge, and Make Decisions* (New York, NY: Oxford University Press, 2007).

[2] D. H. Guston, "Boundary Organizations in Environmental Policy and Science: An Introduction," *Science, Technology, & Human Values* 26, no. 4 (2001): 399-408. S. S. Jasanoff, "Contested Boundaries in Policy-Relevant Science," *Social Studies of Science* 17, no. 2 (1987): 195-230.

[3] For a more complete discussion of boundaries in knowledge domains, see T. F. Gieryn, "Boundaries of Science," in S. Jasanoff et al., eds., *The Handbook of Science and Technology Studies* (Cambridge, MA: MIT Press, 1995).

[4] E. F. Vail, "Knowledge Mapping: Getting Started with Knowledge Management," *Information Systems Management* 16 (1999): 10-23.

[5] H. Douglas, *Science, Policy, and the Value-Free Ideal* (Pittsburgh, PA: University of Pittsburgh Press, 2009).

[6] www.cheerios.com.

[7] S. C. Zehr, "Scientists' Representations of Uncertainty," In S. M. Friedman, S. Dunwoody, and C. L. Rogers, eds., *Communicating Uncertainty: Media Coverage of New and Controversial Science* (Mahwah, NJ: Lawrence Erlbaum Associates, 1999), 3-21.

[8] www.census.gov.

[9] C. Miller, "Hybrid Management: Boundary Organizations, Science Policy, and Environmental Governance in the Climate Regime," *Science, Technology, & Human Values* 26, no. 4 (2001): 478-500.

[10] C. A. Miller, "Civic Epistemologies: Constituting Knowledge and Order in Political Communities," *Sociology Compass* 2, no. 6 (2008): 1896-1919.

[11] B. Wynne, "Misunderstanding Science?: The Public Reconstruction of Science and Technology," in A. Irwin and B. Wynne,

eds., *Misunderstood Misunderstanding: Social Identities and the Public Uptake of Science* (Cambridge, UK: Cambridge University Press, 2003), 19-46.

[12] R. Whitley, *The Intellectual and Social Organization of the Sciences* (Oxford, UK: Oxford University Press, 2000).

[13] T. A. Muñoz-Erickson, "Co-Production of Knowledge–action Systems in Urban Sustainable Governance: The KASA Approach," *Environmental Science & Policy*, 37 (2014): 182-191.

[14] United Nations Framework Convention on Climate Change. The text can be found online at: http://unfccc.int/files/essential_background/background_publications_htmlpdf/application/pdf/conveng.pdf

[15] An example of a U.S. national inventory can be found online at: https://www.epa.gov/sites/production/files/2017-02/documents/2017_complete_report.pdf

[16] A. E. Clarke and J. H. Fujimura, "What Tools? Which Jobs? Why Right?" in A. E. Clarke and J. H. Fujimura, eds., *The Right Tools for the Job: At Work in Twentieth-Century Life Sciences* (Princeton, NJ: Princeton University Press, 1992), 3-44.

[17] H. M. Collins, "What Is Tacit Knowledge?" in T. Schatzki, et al., eds., *The Practice Turn in Contemporary Theory* (New York, NY: Routledge, 2001), 107-119.

[18] For a discussion of various kinds of ignorance and non-knowledge, see: M. Gross, "The Unknown in Process Dynamic Connections of Ignorance, Non-Knowledge and Related Concepts," *Current Sociology* 55, no. 5 (2007): 742-759.

[19] L. Busch, *Standards: Recipes for Reality* (Cambridge, MA: MIT Press, 2011).

[20] C. A. Miller, "Civic Epistemologies: Constituting Knowledge and Order in Political Communities," *Sociology Compass* 2, no. 6 (2008): 1896-1919.

[21] S. Jasanoff and S. H. Kim, "Containing the Atom: Sociotechnical Imaginaries and Nuclear Power in the United States and South Korea," *Minerva* 47, no. 2 (2009): 119-146.

22 C. Miller, "The Dynamics of Framing Environmental Values and Policy: Four Models of Societal Processes," *Environmental Values* 9, no. 2 (2000): 211-233.

23 I. Hacking, "Styles of Scientific Thinking or Reasoning: A New Analytical Tool for Historians and Philosophers of the Sciences," in S. Gavroglu, et al., eds., *Trends in the Historiography of Science* (Amsterdam, Netherlands: Springer, 1994), 31-48.

24 S. Jasanoff, *Designs on Nature: Science and Democracy in Europe and the United States* (Princeton, NJ: Princeton University Press, 2005). S. Shackely, "Epistemic Lifestyles in Climate Change Modeling," in C. Miller and P. Edwards, eds.), *Changing the Atmosphere* (Cambridge, MA: MIT Press, 2001).

25 I. Hacking, "Styles of Scientific Thinking or Reasoning: A New Analytical Tool for Historians and Philosophers of the Sciences," in S. Gavroglu, et al., eds., *Trends in the Historiography of Science* (Amsterdam, Netherlands: Springer, 1994), 31-48.

26 G. C. Bowker, and S. L. Star, *Sorting Things Out: Classification and Its Consequences* (Cambridge, MA: MIT Press, 2008).

27 S. Jasanoff and S. H. Kim, "Containing the Atom: Sociotechnical Imaginaries and Nuclear Power in the United States and South Korea," *Minerva* 47, no. 2 (2009): 119-146.

28 C. Miller, "Interrogating the Civic Epistemology of American Democracy: Stability and Instability in the 2000 U.S. Presidential Election," *Social Studies of Science* 34, no. 4 (2004): 501-530.

29 B. Crona and Ö Bodin, "Power Asymmetries in Small-Scale Fisheries: A Barrier to Governance Transformability?" *Ecology and Society* 15, no. 4 (2010): 32.265.

30 S. Jasanoff, ed., *States of Knowledge: The Co-Production of Science and Social Order* (London, UK: Routledge, 2004).

31 See, for example: S. Jasanoff and B. Wynne, "Science and Decision Making," in *Human Choice and the Climate Change – Vol. 1: The Societal Framework* (Columbus, OH: Battelle Press, 1998).

32 S. Jasanoff, *The Fifth Branch: Science Advisers as Policymakers* (Cambridge, MA: Harvard University Press, 1990). S. Hilgartner, *Science on State: Expert Advice as Public Drama* (Stanford, CA: Stanford University Press, 2000).

[33] T. A. Muñoz-Erickson, B. Aguilar-González, M. R. R. Loeser, and T. D. Sisk, "A Framework to Evaluate Ecological and Social Outcomes of Collaborative Management: Lessons from Implementation with a Northern Arizona Collaborative Group," *Environmental Management* 45, no. 1 (2009): 132-144.

[34] D. W. Cash, "Distributed Assessment Systems: An Emerging Paradigm of Research, Assessment, and Decision Making for Environmental Change," *Global Environmental Change* 10, no. 4 (2000): 241-244. T. A. Muñoz-Erickson, "Co-Production of Knowledge–action Systems in Urban Sustainable Governance: The KASA Approach," *Environmental Science & Policy*, 37 (2014): 182-191.

CHAPTER 3: DESIGNING KNOWLEDGE STYSTEMS THAT WORK

[1] B. Latour and S. Woolgar, *Laboratory Life: The Construction of Scientific Facts* (Princeton, NJ: Princeton University Press, 2013).

[2] Some analysts have referred to this coupling as a knowledge or knowledge management lifecycle. See, e.g.: J. Birkinshaw and T. Sheehan, "Managing the Knowledge Lifecycle," *MIT Sloan Management Review* 44, no. 1 (2002): 75. M. Evans, K. Dalkir, and C. Bidian, "A Holistic View of the Knowledge Lifecycle: The Knowledge Management Cycle (KMC) Model," in *Leading Issues in Knowledge Management*, Vol. 2 (2015), 7.

[3] S. Solomon, ed., *Climate Change 2007 – The Physical Science Basis: Working Group I Contribution to the Fourth Assessment Report of the IPCC*, Vol. 4 Cambridge, UK: Cambridge University Press, 2007).

[4] The report can be found online at: http://www.fda.gov/Food/GuidanceRegulation/GuidanceDocumentsRegulatoryInformation/LabelingNutrition/ucm063113.htm

[5] www.census.gov.

CHAPTER 4: WHEN DIFFERENT WAYS OF KNOWING
CONFLICT

1 H. Tsoukas, *Complex Knowledge: Studies in Organizational Epistemology* (Cambridge, UK: Oxford University Press, 2005).

2 D. H. Guston, *Between Politics and Science: Assuring the Integrity and Productivity of Research* (Cambridge, UK: Cambridge University Press, 2007).

3 D. MacKenzie, *An Engine, Not a Camera: How Financial Models Shape Markets* (Cambridge, MA: MIT Press, 2008).

4 S. Jasanoff, *The Fifth Branch: Science Advisers as Policymakers* (Cambridge, MA: Harvard University Press, 1990).

5 A. A. Daemmrich, *Pharmacopolitics: Drug Regulation in the United States and Germany* (Philadelphia, PA: Chemical Heritage Foundation, 2004).

6 S. Shackley and B. Wynne, "Integrating Knowledges for Climate Change: Pyramids, Nets, and Uncertainties," *Global Environmental Change* 5, no. 2 (1995): 113-126.

7 P. N. Edwards *A Vast Machine: Computer Models, Climate Data, and the Politics of Global Warming* (Cambridge, MA: MIT Press, 2010).

8 S. Shackley, P. Young, S. Parkinson, and B. Wynne, "Uncertainty, Complexity, and Concepts of Good Science in Climate Change Modelling: Are GCMs the Best Tools?" *Climatic Change* 38, no. 2 (1998): 159-205.

9 S. Beck, M. Borie, J. Chilvers, A. Esguerra, K. Heubach, M. Hulme, R. Lidskog, E. Lövbrand, E. Marquard, C. Miller, and T. Nadim, "Towards a Reflexive Turn in the Governance of Global Environmental Expertise. The Cases of the IPCC and the IPBES," *GAIA-Ecological Perspectives for Science and Society* 23, no. 2 (2014): 80-87.

10 R. Swart, L. Bernstein, M. Ha-Duong, and A. Petersen, "Agreeing to Disagree: Uncertainty Management in Assessing Climate Change, Impacts, and Responses by the IPCC," *Climatic Change* 92, no. 1 (2009): 1-29.

[11] S. Beck and T. Forsyth, "Co-Production and Democratizing Global Environmental Expertise," in S. Hiltgartner, C. Miller, and R. Hagendijk, eds., *Science and Democracy: Making Knowledge and Making Power in the Biosciences and Beyond* (New York, NY: Routledge, 2015), 113.

[12] P. N. Edwards and S. H. Schneider, "Self-Governance and Peer Review in Science-for-Policy: The Case of the IPCC Second Assessment Report," in C. A. Miller and P. N. Edwards, eds., *Changing the Atmosphere: Expert Knowledge and Environmental Governance* (Cambridge, MA: MIT Press, 2001), 219-246.

[13] A. Agarwal and S. Narain, *Global Warming in an Unequal World: A Case of Environmental Colonialism* (Delhi, India: Centre for Science and Environment, 1991).

[14] C. Miller, T. Muñoz-Erickson, and C. Monfreda, "Knowledge Systems Analysis," Report #10-05, Consortium for Science, Policy & Outcomes, 2010.

[15] Diane Vaughan's account of the go/no-go decision by NASA to launch the *Challenger* space shuttle is perhaps the most extensive discussion of a single decision and the complex, dynamic knowledge infrastructures and processes that fed into it: D. Vaughan, *The Challenger Launch Decision: Risky Technology, Culture, and Deviance at NASA* (Chicago, IL: University of Chicago Press, 1997).

[16] T. M. Porter, *Trust in Numbers: The Pursuit of Objectivity in Science and Public Life* (Princeton, NJ: Princeton University Press, 1996). D. MacKenzie, "The Credit Crisis as a Problem in the Sociology of Knowledge," *American Journal of Sociology* 116, no. 6 (2011): 1778-1841. D. MacKenzie, "Knowledge Production in Financial Markets: Credit Default Swaps, the ABX and the Subprime Crisis," *Economy and Society* 41, no. 3 (2012): 335-359.

[17] See, e.g.: C. A. Miller, "The Dynamics of Framing Environmental Values and Policy: Four Models of Societal Processes," *Environmental Values* 9, no. 2 (2000): 211-233. S. Jasanoff, "Compelling Knowledge in Public Decisions," in L. A. Brooks, S. D. Vandeveer, eds., *Saving the Seas: Values, Scientists, and International Governance* (College Park, MD: Maryland Sea Grant, 1997), 229-52.

[18] A. Iles, "Making Seafood Sustainable: Merging Consumption and Citizenship in the United States," *Science & Public Policy* 31, no. 2 (2004).

[19] See also: T. A. Muñoz-Erickson, "Co-production of Knowledge-Action Systems in Urban Sustainable Governance: The KASA Approach," *Environmental Science & Policy* 37 (2014): 182-191.

[20] M. M. Robertson, "The Nature that Capital can See: Science, State, and Market in the Commodification of Ecosystem Services," *Environment and Planning D: Society and Space* 24, no. 3 (2006): 367-387. P. D. Hirsch, W. M. Adams, J. P. Brosius, A. Zia, N. Bariola, and J. L. Dammert, "Acknowledging Conservation Trade-Offs and Embracing Complexity," *Conservation Biology* 25, no. 2 (2011): 259-264.

[21] F. Berkes, "Evolution of Co-Management: Role of Knowledge Generation, Bridging Organizations and Social Learning," *Journal of Environmental Management* 90, no. 5 (2009): 1692-1702.

[22] C. Miller, "Knowledge and Accountability in Global Governance," in M. A. Tétreault and R. L. Teske, *Partial Truths and the Politics of Community* (Columbia, SC: University of South Carolina Press, 2003), 315-341.

[23] W. V. Reid, F. Berkes, T. J. Wilbanks, and D. Capistrano, eds., *Bridging Scales and Knowledge Systems: Concepts and Applications in Ecosystem Assessment* (Washington, DC: Island Press, 2006).

[24] A. Agrawal, "Dismantling the Divide between Indigenous and Scientific Knowledge," *Development and Change* 26, no. 3 (1995): 413-439.

[25] C. Miller and P. Erickson, "The Politics of Bridging Scales and Epistemologies: Science and Democracy in Global Environmental Governance," in W. V. Reid, F. Berkes, T. J. Wilbanks, and D. Capistrano, eds., *Bridging Scales and Knowledge Systems: Concepts and Applications in Ecosystem Assessment* (Washington, DC: Island Press, 2006).

[26] B. A. Bimber, *The Politics of Expertise in Congress* (Buffalo, NY: SUNY Press, 1992).

[27] S. Jasanoff, "What Judges Should Know about the Sociology of Science," *Jurimetrics* 32, no. 3 (1992): 345-359.

[28] Four of these (hybridization, deconstruction, boundary work, and jurisdictional orchestration) are more fully described by Clark Miller, who applies them to the example of the climate knowledge system: C. Miller, "Hybrid Management Boundary Organizations, Science Policy, and Environmental Governance in the Climate Regime," *Science, Technology & Human Values* 26, no. 4 (2001): 399-408. We have chosen to separate out an additional element (credibility performance) due to its significance in recent studies, which we cite below.

[29] S. Jasanoff, *Science at the Bar: Law, Science, and Technology in America* (Cambridge, MA: Harvard University Press, 1995).

[30] K. R. Eschenfelder and C. A. Miller, "What Information Should State Wildlife Agencies Provide on Their CWD Websites?" *Human Dimensions of Wildlife* 11, no. 3 (2006): 221-223.

[31] M. Jacob, "Boundary Work in Contemporary Science Policy: A Review," *Prometheus* 23, no. 2 (2005): 195-207.

[32] S. Jasanoff, *The Fifth Branch: Science Advisers as Policymakers* (Cambridge, MA: Harvard University Press, 1990).

[33] T. Gieryn, "Boundary-Work and the Demarcation of Science from Non-Science," *American Sociological Review* 48, no. 6 (1983): 781-795.

[34] S. Hilgartner, *Science on Stage: Expert Advice as Public Drama* (Stanford, CA: Stanford University Press, 2000).

[35] T. Gieryn, *Cultural Boundaries of Science: Credibility on the Line* (Chicago, IL: University of Chicago Press, 1999).

[36] S. Shapin, *A Social History of Truth* (Chicago, IL: The University of Chicago Press, 1994).

[37] S. Epstein, *Impure Science: AIDS, Activism, and the Politics of Knowledge* (Berkeley, CA: University of California Press, 1996).

[38] S. Shapin, "Cordelia's Love: Credibility and the Social Studies of Science," *Perspectives on Science* 3, no. 3 (1995): 255-275.

39 W. D. Rifkin and B. Martin, "Negotiating Expert Status: Who Gets Taken Seriously," *Technology and Society Magazine* (1997): 30-38.

40 M. Foucault, *Power/Knowledge: Selected Interviews and Other Writings, 1972-1977* (New York, NY: Pantheon, 1980). A. S. Mathews, *Instituting Nature: Authority, Expertise, and Power in Mexican Forests* (Cambridge, MA: MIT Press, 2011). W. K. Storey, *Science and Power in Colonial Mauritius* (Rochester, NY: University of Rochester Press, 1997).

41 J. C. Scott, *Seeing like a State: How Certain Schemes to Improve the Human Condition have Failed* (New Haven, CT: Yale University Press, 1998).

42 A. Rich, *Think Tanks, Public Policy, and the Politics of Expertise* (Cambridge, UK: Cambridge University Press, 2005). S. Jasanoff, "Science and Citizenship: A New Synergy," *Science & Public Policy* 31, no. 2 (2004).

43 S. P. Hays, *Conservation and the Gospel of Efficiency: The Progressive Conservation Movement, 1890–1920* (Pittsburgh, PA: University of Pittsburgh Press, 1957).

44 S. Jasanoff, *Science at the Bar: Law, Science, and Technology in America* (Cambridge, MA: Harvard University Press, 1995).

45 T. M. Porter, *Trust in Numbers: The Pursuit of Objectivity in Science and Public Life* (Princeton, NJ: Princeton University Press, 1996).

46 S. Jasanoff, *The Fifth Branch: Science Advisers as Policymakers* (Cambridge, MA: Harvard University Press, 1990).

47 S. Jasanoff, *Science at the Bar: Law, Science, and Technology in America* (Cambridge, MA: Harvard University Press, 1995).

48 S. Jasanoff, "Contested Boundaries in Policy-Relevant Science," *Social Studies of Science* 17, no. 2 (1987): 195-230.

49 S. Epstein, *Impure Science: AIDS, Activism, and the Politics of Knowledge* (Berkeley, CA: University of California Press, 1996).

50 S. Jasanoff, "Science, Politics, and the Renegotiation of Expertise at EPA," *Osiris* 7 (1992): 194-217.

CHAPTER 5: CREATING A KNOWLEDGE-AWARE ORGANIZATION

[1] Y. Ezrahi, *The Descent of Icarus: Science and the Transformation of Contemporary Democracy* (Cambridge, MA: Harvard University Press, 1990).

[2] S. Jasanoff, ed., *States of Knowledge: The Co-Production of Science and the Social Order* (London, UK: Routledge, 2004). R. B. Parks, P. C. Baker, L. Kiser, R. Oakerson, E. Ostrom, V. Ostrom, S. L. Percy, M. B. Vandivort, G. P. Whitaker, and R. Wilson, "Consumers as Co-Producers of Public Services: Some Economic and Institutional Considerations," *Policy Studies Journal* 9, no. 7 (1981): 1001-1011. B. Latour, *The Pasteurization of France* (Cambridge, MA: Harvard University Press, 1993).

[3] S. van der Hel, "New Science for Global Sustainability? The Institutionalisation of Knowledge Co-Production in Future Earth," *Environmental Science & Policy* 61 (2016): 165-175.

[4] J. Brand-Miller and K. Foster-Powell, *The New Glucose Revolution Low GI Guide to Diabetes: The Only Authoritative Guide to Managing Diabetes Using the Glycemic Index* (Boston, MA: Da Capo Press, 2005).

[5] F. Berkes, "Evolution of Co-Management: Role of Knowledge Generation, Bridging Organizations and Social Learning," *Journal of Environmental Management* 90, no. 5 (2009): 1692-1702.

[6] D. W. Cash, W. C. Clark, F. Alcock, N. M. Dickson, N. Eckley, D. H. Guston, J. Jäger, and R. B. Mitchell, "Knowledge Systems for Sustainable Development," *Proceedings of the National Academy of Sciences* 100, no. 14 (2003): 8086-8091.

[7] G. Grabher, O. Ibert, and S. Flohr, "The Neglected King: The Customer in the New Knowledge Ecology of Innovation," *Economic Geography* 84, no. 3 (2008): 253-280.

[8] A. Kolk, "Trajectories of Sustainability Reporting by MNCs," *Journal of World Business* 45, no. 4 (2010): 367-374.

9 A. Kolk, D. Levy, and J. Pinkse, "Corporate Responses in an Emerging Climate Regime: The Institutionalization and Commensuration of Carbon Disclosure," *European Accounting Review* 17, no. 4 (2008): 719-745.

10 B. Anderson, *Imagined Communities: Reflections on the Origin and Spread of Nationalism* (London, UK: Verso Books, 2006).

11 S. Shapin, "Cordelia's Love: Credibility and the Social Studies of Science," *Perspectives on Science* 3, no. 3 (1995): 255-275.

12 S. Jassanoff, "Ordering Knowledge, Ordering Society," in S. Jasanoff, ed., *States of Knowledge: The Co-Production of Science and Social Order* (London, UK: Routledge, 2004), 13-45.

13 C. A. Miller, "Climate Science and the Making of a Global Political Order," in S. Jasanoff, ed., *States of Knowledge: The Co-Production of Science and Social Order* (London, UK: Routledge, 2004), 46-66.

14 T. S. Kuhn, *The Structure of Scientific Revolutions* (Chicago, IL: University of Chicago Press, 1962).

15 G. Bowker and S. L. Star, *Sorting Things Out: Classification and its Consequences* (Cambridge, MA: MIT Press, 1999).

16 C. Waterton and B. Wynne, "Knowledge and Political Order in the European Environment Agency," in S. Jasanoff, ed., *States of Knowledge: The Co-Production of Science and Social Order* (London, UK: Routledge, 2004), 87-108.

17 Y. Ezrahi, "Science and the Political Imagination in Contemporary Democracies," in S. Jasanoff, ed., *States of Knowledge: The Co-Production of Science and Social Order* (London, UK: Routledge, 2004).

18 S. Jasanoff, "Harmonization — The Politics of Reasoning Together," in *The Politics of Chemical Risk: Scenarios for a Regulatory Future* (Amsterdam, Netherlands: Springer, 1998).

19 American Society for Civil Engineering, *The New Orleans Hurricane Protection System: What Went Wrong and Why: A Report* (Reston, VA: ASCE, 2007).

CONCLUSION: TAKING CONTROL OF KNOWLEDGE

[1] Cathy O'Neil, *Weapons of Math Destruction: How Big Data Increases Inequality and Threatens Democracy* (New York, NY: Broadway Books, 2017). Ed Finn, *What Algorithms Want: Imagination in the Age of Computing* (Cambridge, MA: MIT Press, 2017).

ABOUT THE AUTHORS

Clark A. Miller designs and analyzes knowledge systems for organizations looking to improve sustainability, resilience, and social responsibility. Over the past 25 years, he has collaborated with cities, businesses, universities, and international institutions to evaluate and rethink how they create and use knowledge. Since 2015, he has helped lead Arizona State University's new interdisciplinary School for the Future of Innovation in Society as well as several major knowledge innovation initiatives at the intersection of engineering, policy, and social transformation.

Tischa A. Muñoz-Erickson designs and builds transdisciplinary networks, programs, and tools to co-produce knowledge and strategies for resilience and sustainability transitions among diverse research, policy, and civic partners in communities and cities across the United States, Latin America, and Caribbean. She helped found and lead the U.S. Forest Service International Urban Field Station, the San Juan Long-Term Research Area (ULTRA), and the NSF Urban Resilience to Extreme Weather-Related Events Sustainability Research Network (UREx SRN), all of which are strongly informed by ideas of knowledge systems design. She is a social research scientist at the U.S. Forest Service International Institute of Tropical Forestry. All views presented in this book are her own and not those of the U.S. Forest Service.

To stay connected with the research and ideas that went into writing this book, visit:
http://designingknowledge.com

45593101R00098

Made in the USA
San Bernardino, CA
30 July 2019